GLOBAL ISSUES & SUSTAINABLE SOLUTIONS

POPULATION, POVERTY, CONSUMPTION, CONFLICT, AND THE ENVIRONMENT

Devin Hibbard, M.P.A.

Gilda Wheeler, M.Ed.

Wendy Church, Ph.D.

Global Issues and Sustainable Solutions:
Population, Poverty, Consumption, Conflict, and the Environment

By Devin Hibbard, M.P.A.; Gilda Wheeler, M.Ed.; and Wendy Church, Ph.D.

Design and layout by Dinko Bajric and Gilda Wheeler
Editorial assistance by Kim Rakow Bernier and Heidi Radenovic
Copy edited by Kris Fulsaas
An earlier edition of this guide was written by John Goekler, Liam Moriarty, Devin Hibbard, and Ian Byington.

Produced with the generous support of the Phoebe Haas Charitable Trust.

We gratefully acknowledge the following individuals who offered their expertise and review in the preparation of this guide: James Bennett, Louise Chawla, Ph.D., John DeGraaf, Dee Dickinson, Ara Erickson, Arni Isaksson, Marilyn Knight, Terry Leitzell, Nancy McKay, Lee Minto, Jackie Sherris, Ph.D., Dr. Debra Sullivan, and the following teachers who offered helpful critique and suggestions: Eileen Berlin, Wendy Ewbank, Scott Jamieson, Larry Steele, and Ben Wheeler.

Cover photo credits: Harvesting wheat from USDA, Guatemalan children from Water Partners International, People and car courtesy of National Biodiesel Board, Snow leopard by Dennis Conner courtesy of International Snow Leopard Trust.

Printed on recycled paper
ISBN # 0-9711005-3-5

Facing the Future: People and the Planet is a nonprofit organization providing global issues and sustainability resources and action opportunities for teachers, students, and the public. For more information about *Facing the Future: People and the Planet* and to order copies of this guide, visit our website at www.facingthefuture.org or contact us at:

Facing the Future: People and the Planet
811 First Avenue, Suite 454
Seattle, WA 98104
(206) 264-1503
Email: office@facingthefuture.org

www.facingthefuture.org

Contents

This publication is in honor of Priscilla B. Collins, whose conviction about the value of education continues to inspire our work.

SUSTAINABILITY

Global Issues and Sustainability

Never has our world been so interconnected. People can travel halfway around the planet in a matter of hours. Businesses based in one country can make and sell products in other countries. Students from different countries can collaborate on projects in "virtual classrooms." Many of these connections and issues are positive, such as today's high-speed technology that makes instant communication possible throughout the world.

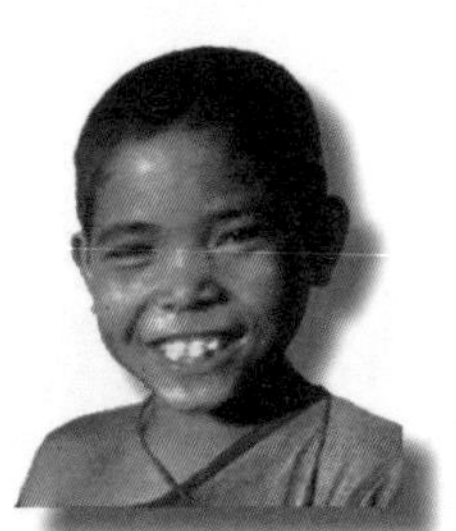

On the other hand, experts think some globally connected issues are so serious that they threaten the health, happiness, and productivity of people and societies around the world. Some of these **global issues** include rapid population growth, environmental damage, high resource **consumption**, national and international conflict, and the growing number of people living in poverty.

Why might these global issues present a real challenge? One reason is that the Earth can produce resources at only a certain rate. Increases in human population and consumption strain our ability to meet the growing demand on the Earth's resources.

The impact of humankind on the Earth depends partly on the kinds of resources we use. For example, it takes most trees twenty to one hundred years to grow to maturity. Trees are considered a **renewable resource** because with forest management, new trees can grow and provide wood products. However, trees grown for human use in tree farms don't always provide all of the benefits that a natural forest offers, such as species diversity and habitat for animals.

Unlike trees, coal is considered a **nonrenewable resource** because it takes thousands of years to form. Once it is used, it can't be created again within the scope of human lifetimes. In addition, when coal is burned, it creates air pollution and releases **carbon dioxide**, which can damage the environment.

We can ask some key questions to determine the degree to which a resource is renewable or nonrenewable. These questions apply not only to forests and coal but also to other resources such as air, water, and soil for growing food:

- How much of the resource exists?
- How much of the resource is being used now and what will be the future demand for it?
- How quickly does the resource regenerate?
- What are the impacts of producing and using the resource?

A helpful way to think about renewable and nonrenewable resources is through the concept of **sustainability**.

The People Who Ate People

Easter Island is one place that wasn't sustainable and where people committed ecological suicide. This means their population grew until there were more people than the island could support. When people first got to Easter Island, in 400 CE (**Common Era**), there were forests and many wild animals. Because the island provided a good life for the people, the population increased, they developed a sophisticated Polynesian culture, and they erected many stone monuments.

Eventually there were more people than the island could support: the forests were cut down, animals were hunted to extinction, and vegetation was lost. At this point, there was only one resource left to use as food—humans! Many of the people on the island began eating those who had died of starvation.

When European ships landed on Easter Island in 1722, explorers found warring bands of people on a destroyed island.[1]

What Is Sustainability?

Sustainability means that we meet our own needs without limiting the ability of future generations to meet their needs.[2] How do we know if something is sustainable? There are three main areas of sustainability: environment, society, and economy.[3] To be sustainable, each of these elements should be healthy. Improvements to any one of these should not make any of the others worse.

For example, imagine that you are a fisherman living in a small village. Your family has lived in this village and fished for generations. Everyone in your family, as far back as your great-grandmother, has caught 1,000 fish each year to sell at the local market. The family fishing boat has been passed down to you.

Now there is a new net you could buy that will allow you to catch 1,200 fish each year. The net drags behind your boat and scoops up the fish. Using the net will allow you to catch more fish for the next ten years. However, over time, as you and other people in the village take more fish each year, there will be fewer adult fish to reproduce and the total number of fish will decrease.

Even though you can catch more fish in the short term, using the net may be unsustainable for future generations. The number of fish available for your children to catch won't be the same number you can catch now. Also, if there aren't enough fish to sell, the economy of the village will be hurt and your children may not be able to support themselves by fishing.

A sustainable solution to this challenge should protect and enhance the environment, the economy, and society. You want to ensure that the environment is healthy and that enough fish can mature and reproduce. You also need to be sure that the economy is strong so that you and the other fishermen can make a living. Finally, you want to make sure that the society remains vibrant by including everyone in decisions about fishing and protecting the diversity of culture, language, religion, art, and tradition.

Everything Is Connected

Have you ever seen a mobile? The objects are separate and move in different directions, but they are interconnected and in balance with each other. Touch

Like a mobile, global issues are interconnected. Graph by *Facing the Future: People and the Planet*

one piece, and all the others move. Cut one string, and the whole thing gets thrown off balance.

What's in a Name?

When talking about countries around the world, people use many different terms, which can sometimes get confusing. Here are some of the terms used in this guide and what they mean:

The terms **developed** and **developing countries** refer to the differences in levels of wealth and standard of living between different countries around the world. Developed countries have higher average per-person incomes; Japan, Canada, the United States, Australia, New Zealand, and countries in western Europe are considered developed countries. Countries from the former U.S.S.R. and eastern Europe are not considered either developing or developed. All other countries are called developing.[4]

The World Bank classifies countries based on per-person gross national income. Low-income countries are those with a per-person income of $735 or less per year. Middle-income countries include those with a yearly per-person income from $736 to $9,075. High-income countries are those with a yearly per-person income of $9,076 or more.[5] In this guide, we sometimes refer to low-income countries as poor and high-income countries as rich.

Other terms used by some people to describe countries are first, second, and third world; global north and global south; and high-consuming and low-consuming countries.

Some of these terms can be misleading at times. For example, some countries that are considered to be developing are not actually experiencing economic growth at all, while many developed countries have economies that continue to grow. In addition, these terms could imply that all countries should try to become developed. In fact, many experts and people in developing countries think some developed countries are actually overdeveloped and need to reduce their use of resources. Finally, categorization of a country as rich or poor doesn't acknowledge richness or poverty of culture, tradition, family life, and countless other factors.

While none of these terms are perfect, this guide most often uses the terms developed/developing and rich/poor when highlighting differences between countries.

The environment is interconnected in the same way as that mobile. Every type of organism, from bacteria to whales to people, is part of a food web that depends on healthy habitats to survive.

The human-made environment is interconnected, too. The shoes you're wearing right now may have been made in Southeast Asia, your pants in Central America, your watch in Japan. Chances are, the sandwich you eat is made with wheat from Canada, tuna fish from Chile, lettuce from Texas, and tomatoes from Mexico.

Just as sustainability connects environment, economy, and society, global issues are also interconnected. Population growth, poverty, consumption, conflicts, and the environment all affect each other in many ways. Challenges or solutions in one area can have a dramatic impact on the others.

For example, as population increases, more resources are used and often the environment is damaged. In developing countries, the environment is affected when families clear forests for firewood or farmland. In developed countries, people consume a large amount of resources such as food, water, oil, and iron. That can also have a big impact on the environment.

Once you become aware of how these issues are connected, you can see how working toward sustainability in one area can have positive impacts on all of the others.

Signs of Sustainability

When we think about sustainability for the whole planet, we can ask some key questions:

- What is the maximum human population the planet can support?
- How much damage can the environment absorb?
- What would be the effects of distributing food and water more equitably?
- How much and what kind of resource consumption can the Earth support?

The difficulty in figuring out sustainability is that there is no single answer to any of these questions. In fact, the answers depend on lots of factors. Sustainability isn't just a matter of having enough food. For humans, it is also a matter of **quality of life**, which may include a peaceful society, a rich culture, a satisfying life, and cultural pursuits such as art, music, and athletics.

Figuring out the sustainable level of population depends on how many resources each person needs and wants to use to have a satisfying life. The Earth could support many more people who consume resources at a moderate level than it could if everyone on the planet consumed a high level of resources. In fact, how people define what makes life satisfying is different in many places, but there is increasing evidence that having more money above a certain income level and consuming more things don't make people any happier.[6]

Because the world is more and m
sustainability means considering the n
planet—and all 6.3 billion people on it. P
world have different levels of income, cc
amounts of resources, have different cu
and live in different geographic regions,
global sustainability is complicated.

Sustainable Solutions

The good news is that many sustainable practices are already being used today. We can make choices each day to increase sustainability in many areas. Some of those choices are small, such as riding a bike or walking to school rather than driving, recycling so we can keep reusable material out of the landfill, or turning off lights and turning down the heat at night to conserve fuel.

Some choices are larger, such as ones that we all make as we get older. What size family will you have? Will you support government policies that encourage sustainability? Will you buy products that are more sustainable?

Government policies are also important in achieving greater sustainability. Fortunately, many countries are coming together to discuss and implement practices that will lead to greater sustainability.[7] For example, many nations have signed the **Kyoto Protocol** to address **global warming** caused by carbon dioxide emissions.

Also, many renewable energy technologies—wind, **bio-diesel**, solar, hydro, geothermal—are being used by more and more governments and people. Using these will help us live sustainably today without using the resources people may need in the future. However, just as for good health and physical fitness, we need to work at sustainability throughout our lifetime.

We can't solve the sustainability challenges for all future generations or all global cultures. Because we can't predict the challenges that people of the future will face or the things their cultures will value, the people of the future are the only ones who can decide what the right choices are for them. But we can try our best to ensure that future generations have a good set of choices and have what they need to survive and prosper.

Photo by Water Partners International

WHAT'S UP WITH POPULATION, ANYWAY?

If it seems as though there are many more people around these days, you're right. There are more people on highways, more people in line at supermarkets, more people at parks, and maybe even more people in your school.

Even if you live in an area that isn't growing all that much, the human population of the rest of the planet is growing incredibly fast.

Just fifty years ago, when your grandparents were young adults, there were 2.5 billion people living on Earth. It took all of human history—from prehistoric time until after World War II—for human population to reach that level.

Now there are more than 6.3 billion people, and we're adding about 82 million each year.[8] That's like adding another Germany every year or another San Francisco every three and a half days.[9] Experts believe that by 2050, there will be almost 9 billion people living in the area where 6 billion of us live now.[10]

You don't have to look very far to see the effects of there being more and more people on the planet. Every day on the news, there are stories of **global warming**, forests being cut down, endangered wildlife, and changing migration patterns. We hear about crime, pollution, poverty, overcrowding, and more.

Growing Population, Growing Demand

The human population grows whenever more people are born in a year than die. Our population would stay almost constant if each family had two children, one to replace each parent.[11] Currently, about 139 million people are born each year and 57 million die. The difference produces the global population increase.[12]

You Do the Math!
Lower rates but higher numbers. What's up with that?

Population experts say that the rate of population increase is going down. Yet there are more people in the world each year. Let's look at how this works.

Imagine you live on an island with 10,000 people. Let's say the growth rate for this year is 10 percent. That means there are 1,000 more people, or 11,000 total, at the end of the year.

Now let's say the next year the growth rate is only 1 percent. That means 110 people are added to the population, raising the population to 11,110. Even though the rate went down from 10 percent to 1 percent, the overall number still goes up. Even if we slow world population growth rate, we're still adding more people each year than are dying.

	Population	Growth Rate	Increase	Total Population
Year 1:	10,000	10%	1,000	11,000
Year 2:	11,000	1%	110	11,110

How does this work in the real world? Let's look at Brazil. When Brazil's population of 176.5 million people adds 1.3 percent this year, that's 2.3 million more people, for a total of 178.8 million. If Brazil's population increases only 1 percent the next year, they'll add around 1.8 million people. Now they'll have 180.6 million people overall, even though their rate went down.[13]

To see this increase in action, check out the Population Clock on *Facing the Future*'s website at www.popinfo.org.

Indeed, in many parts of the world, people have quite large families. It's no coincidence that the places in the world where people are poorest are also the places where population is growing fastest. People in poorer countries know that having a big family can be their key to survival.

In some **developing countries**, there is no social security system, health care is expensive, and many people live in **extreme poverty**. In fact, of the 4.4 billion

A woman tests a solar cooker at an appropriate technology center in India.
Photo by Gene Thiemann/Lutheran World Relief, courtesy of Photoshare

people living in developing countries, nearly 60 percent don't have **basic sanitation**, almost one-third do not have access to clean water, and one-quarter lack proper housing. Twenty percent don't have access to modern health services, and 20 percent of children do not attend school through grade five.[14] People in this kind of poverty rely on a large extended family to make a living and to care for the elderly.

People living in rural areas need help to gather cooking fuel, haul water, grow their food, and tend their livestock. Where disease and malnutrition kill many children before they grow up, large families are often seen as a necessity.

Families who migrate to the city or families who gain access to health care might continue to have large families for some time until they are assured that they don't need more children to help with survival. When death rates come down quickly because of better health care but family size doesn't drop nearly as fast, population still increases rapidly.

Population is growing in some rich countries, too, but not as fast as in many poor countries. Both birth rates in rich countries and immigration to rich countries contribute to their population growth. Although population isn't growing as fast in rich countries as it is in poor countries, the average person in a rich country consumes many more resources than the average person in a poor country. In fact, a child living in the United States will use as many resources and create as much pollution in one year as eight children living in Indonesia, Peru, or Kenya.[15]

Population Policy Can Make a Difference![16]

The Muslim country of Iran is noted for having a successful population policy. In the 1980s, when Iran was at war with Iraq, the Iranian government encouraged families to have many children, in part because it was felt that a large population would be an advantage in the war. Government policies encouraged large families, and doctors were told not to provide family planning. During this time, women had an average of seven children.

At the end of the 1980s, Iran began to feel the pressure of a rapidly increasing population as the economy slumped and the population was too large for the country's public services. Ayatollah Khomeini, the political and religious leader, decided that Iran needed to address its growing population in order to prosper.

Among the steps taken by the Iranian government were providing free family planning services to all citizens, encouraging families to space their children, educating men about family planning, offering maternity leave for only the first three children per family, and using the media to raise awareness of population growth and family planning. Government policies also focused on lowering infant mortality rates, promoting women's education and employment, and extending social security benefits so families wouldn't feel a need to have a large family to support them in old age.

"Less population, more opportunities, prosperous future."

Between 1986 and 2001, the average number of children per woman dropped from seven to three. The United Nations predicts that by 2010, the population growth rate in Iran will be lower than the rate in the United States. Curbing population growth in Iran has also helped its citizens in many other ways. Iran already faces water scarcity and has to import grain to feed the population. A quickly growing population would have made it more difficult to provide its citizens with food and water.

The example of Iran shows that strong leadership within the government can be an important factor in curbing a rapidly growing population.

So we not only have to think about addressing population growth, we also have to consider the impact that each of us has on the Earth. What kind of environment will we leave for our children and grandchildren?

As population grows from the 6.3 billion people we have today to 9 billion people predicted in 2050[17], all of those people will need food, water, housing, and jobs. They may also want the things you want: cars, video games, skateboards, CD players, and vacations.

The good news is that the latest estimates show the global population growth rate slowing. In 1990, experts predicted there would be 8.5 billion people in 2025. In 1998, those projections were down to 7.8 billion.[18] This is because the number of children born dropped more quickly than predicted, partly due to better access to health care and family planning in countries around the world.[19]

Higher levels of education, improved rights for women, and increased economic opportunity are also related to lowering population growth.[20] When people have more education and higher incomes, they feel more confident about their future. In fact, as families send their children to school, the cost of each child increases, and they tend to limit the number of children they choose to have.[21]

Around the world, many people still depend on large families to survive. At the same time, people in **developed countries** such as the United States are consuming many resources to have all the things they want. Together, we have a major impact on the environment and the planet's resources that support us.

Toward a Stable Population

We can do many things to help bring population to sustainable levels, levels that the Earth can support now and in the future. Some involve individual choices that people can make each day. Government action and social changes toward a stable population require that citizens make their voices heard through voting, actively participating in government, and being involved in their community.

One step that requires government action and international support is making health care and family planning services available to everyone. Evidence shows that people who

Young women and children in Sumba, Indonesia. Photo by Harvey Nelson, courtesy of Photoshare

can choose the number and spacing of their children—and who are confident their children will survive—will have smaller families.[22]

Some changes are social and cultural; these will involve many people changing their attitudes. An example of this is making education available to women and boosting their status in society. Educated women marry later, have fewer children, are more likely to send their children to school, and tend to earn more money to support their families.[23]

Helping families get out of poverty would also help stabilize population, because as people make more money, they often have smaller families and invest in educating their children.

Other steps can involve individual changes in how each one of us decides to live our life. How big a family you have, how large your house is, how much energy you use each day, how much waste you create—these decisions all have an impact. We can make a difference if we want to, once we understand how individual choices affect the big picture.

The choices we all make in the next few decades will determine how quickly we can stabilize population growth and create a sustainable world.

What future do you want to see?

POPULATION THROUGHOUT HISTORY

In just the last forty years, the number of people living on Earth has doubled, from 3 billion to more than 6 billion. Nothing like this has ever happened before.

The Great Wall of China was built during the Qing Dynasty around 220 BCE to keep foreign invaders from capturing food and other resources. Photo from ClickArt

In the Beginning

Back in the Stone Age, more than 12,000 years ago, there were approximately 5 million people on the entire planet. They lived as hunter-gatherers in small tribes. They followed the migrations of animals and the seasonal growth of plants. Population remained stable because almost as many people died as were born.

About 10,000 years ago, that started to change. Over time, people learned to grow plants and raise animals. Farming can produce up to 100 times as much food as will grow wild on the same amount of land. So when people learned to raise animals and crops, they produced much more food.

When there's plenty of food available, a population tends to grow. As people became farmers rather than nomads, the population increased. Shifting from hunting and gathering to farming caused cultural changes, too. People learned how to build walls and large buildings to store and protect their extra food. After a while, people began to live inside those walled settlements.

With extra food, not everyone was needed to work the fields. This allowed people to do other jobs such as being artists, priests, soldiers, and engineers.

As societies became more complex, writing, counting, and measuring developed. People could now keep track of their extra food and money. As economies grew and more food was produced, population grew even faster.

By the birth of Jesus Christ around the year 1 in the **Common Era** (CE), there were about 250 million people on the entire Earth—fewer than the number of people who live just in the United States today.

As towns and cities grew, more food was required to feed the expanding population. When more food was available, the population grew even more. Then they needed more food, which led to more people, and the cycle continued. However, during this early time, the worldwide population remained low because death rates were high. Disease, war, and hunger killed many people. As people began to

Population through the Centuries: How We Got to 6 Billion

Through most of history, the number of deaths has been nearly the same as the number of births. The result? Slow population growth. Then, in the last thousand years, the population curve started to move upward. If current growth rates continue, there will be just under 8 billion people on the planet in 2025.[24]

2-5 million years

6000 B.C.E.

4000 B.C.E.

live closely together in cities, diseases such as measles, smallpox, and bubonic plague broke out and millions of people died.

For example, it's estimated that the population of Europe was cut in half by a plague in the sixth century CE.[25] When plague returned in the fourteenth century CE, the "Black Death," as it was called, killed one-third of the people in Europe.[26]

Famines also killed many people. When bad weather or crop diseases lowered food production, many people starved.

Despite these setbacks, overall population continued to grow slowly. More people were being born than were dying. By the time Christopher Columbus sailed to America in 1492 CE, world population had doubled, since 1 CE, to 500 million people.

The Impacts of Civilization Growth

The increasing population in early times had both positive and negative results.

On the positive side, larger populations with enough food allowed people to specialize in different professions and led to advances in science, health, and technology. Cities grew and developed roads, water systems, and public buildings. Architecture, mathematics, literature, art, and science advanced. For example, the Chinese invented the first compass in the fourth century **Before Common Era** (BCE).[27]

On the negative side, historical evidence indicates that larger populations sometimes outgrew their resources. Civilizations started in areas with lots of resources, such as fertile soil in which to grow crops, freshwater, and forests that provided wood for building and fuel. Using those resources led to prosperity, and prosperity led to growing populations.

As more people needed food, clothing, employment, and shelter, they used up the resources on which they

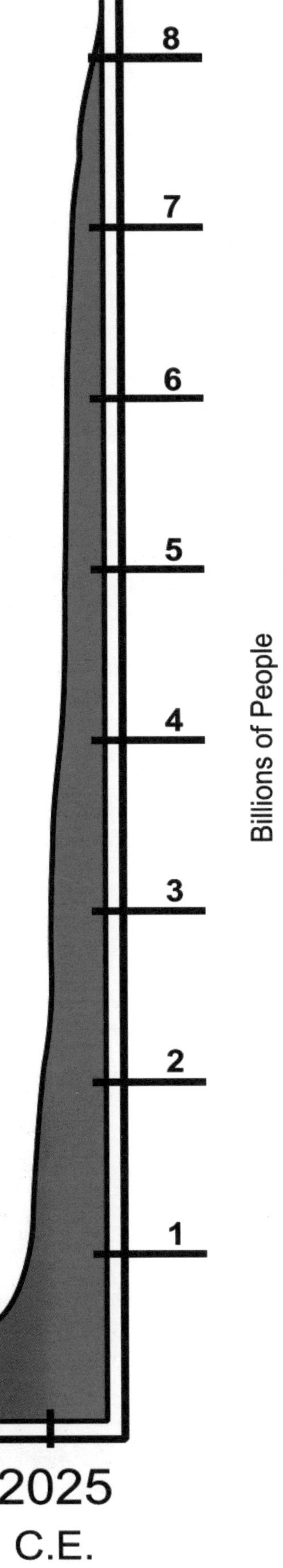

depended. Often, forests were cut down, soils were eroded, and clean water became scarce. That frequently resulted in economic collapse, hunger, war, and migrations of people looking for new places to live.

For example, the societies that arose in the Fertile Crescent (a part of the Middle East from the Nile to the Tigris and Euphrates Rivers) prospered at first. In time, the forests that once covered much of the region were cleared for agriculture, used for firewood, or cut for timber. The area's normally limited rainfall means that vegetation doesn't grow quickly, so goats easily overgrazed the fragile environment. As the forests and grasslands decreased, erosion occurred. Eventually political power and population shifted from the Fertile Crescent to societies farther west, where more rainfall insured that crops grew more quickly.[28]

Europe and the World

In some cases, societies that outgrew their own resources invaded neighboring countries and took their resources. By the fifteenth century, some European cultures began to conquer distant lands in search of even more resources.

In the 1500s, European countries established colonies in Asia, Africa, and the Americas. This brought a flood of new resources to the European continent. Gold, silver, and spices from the colonies made some nations rich, while many of the colonized countries remained poor. Some of the plants the colonists brought back to Europe, such as potatoes and corn, increased food supplies because they grew well in European climates.

The increase in food supply and improvement in sanitation in Europe triggered another burst of population growth. In the 250 years between 1500 and 1750 CE, Europe's population grew as much as it had in the previous 1,500 years.

Between 1600 and 1870 CE, the colonies brought new resources to Europe, but they also acted as a relief valve for population pressures. Though we often read about people moving to the colonies in North America, Africa, and Asia for religious freedom or economic opportunity, crowding and a scarcity of farmland in Europe also contributed to the migration.

Colonial times were often violent, as European colonists used force against native peoples. Across North and South America and Africa, native people were often pushed out of their ancient homes by the newcomers and were sometimes enslaved or murdered in the process. European colonists also unknowingly brought diseases with them. These diseases killed millions of native peoples, who had never been exposed to them before and had little or no resistance to the diseases.[29]

The Industrial Revolution

Resources from European countries' colonies and technological advances of the Industrial Revolution created an economic boom. Beginning in the 1800s, Europeans began using coal, rather than animal labor, wood, or wind, to power their industries. Steam-powered trains and ships allowed goods and raw materials to be transported farther and more quickly than ever before. New machines meant fewer workers could produce even more

Some ancient civilizations abandoned their homes. Is this what happened to the Anasazi, who built cliff dwellings in southwestern U.S.? Photo by John Goekler

food from the same amount of land.

In 1830 CE, there were more than 1 billion people on Earth, and people in Europe began to live longer, healthier lives. By the early 1900s, the discovery that germs cause disease had improved medicine and sanitation. Better water and sewer systems cut back the death toll from communicable diseases. The invention of antibiotics and vaccines controlled many diseases that had been fatal in the past.

European invaders used guns and horses to conquer native civilizations in the Americas, such as the Incan city of Machu Picchu in Peru. Photo by John Goekler

The Modern Era

After World War II, health and sanitation advances were brought to **developing countries**, where 72 percent of the global population lived.[30] Because of improved medicine, sanitation, and health care, deaths from disease fell and many more children survived to adulthood. The rapid fall in the death rate benefited people around the world and created **exponential growth** in global population. India and China, which already had large populations, were two of the areas with the biggest population increase after World War II.[31]

It took all of human history—about 50,000 years—for the global population to reach 1 billion, but only 123 years for it to reach 2 billion. The third billion was added in just 33 years and the next billion in only 14 years. Now we're adding another billion people every 12 to 14 years.[32] Nearly all of this growth will occur in developing countries in Asia, Africa, and Latin America.[33]

The choices we make in the present determine our future; in the next few decades, our choices about population growth will determine whether we have a healthy, sustainable future. The challenge that we now face is how to balance the human population with the resources our planet can provide. We'll need to use our knowledge, resources, technology, and commitment to act locally, nationally, and globally to ensure a healthy and sustainable future.

HOW MANY PEOPLE CAN THE EARTH SUPPORT?

There are certainly many people on the planet right now —twice as many as there were just forty years ago and 82 million more than just one year ago. Even in the time it takes to read this paragraph, about fifty more people will have been added to the planet.[34]

Rice Harvesters in Bhutan. Photo from UN FAO

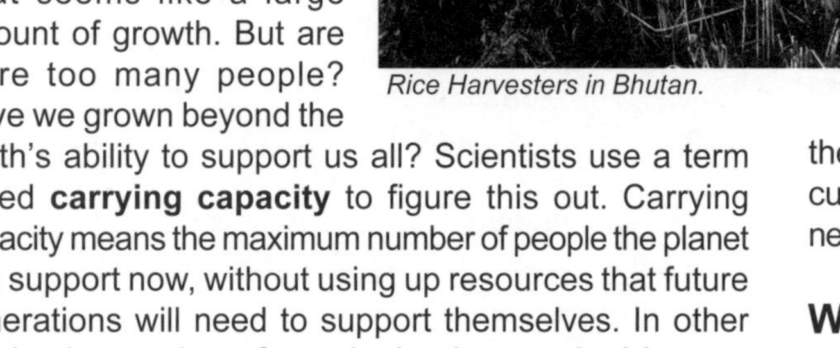

That seems like a large amount of growth. But are there too many people? Have we grown beyond the Earth's ability to support us all? Scientists use a term called **carrying capacity** to figure this out. Carrying capacity means the maximum number of people the planet can support now, without using up resources that future generations will need to support themselves. In other words, the number of people that is **sustainable**—not using resources faster than the Earth can reproduce them.

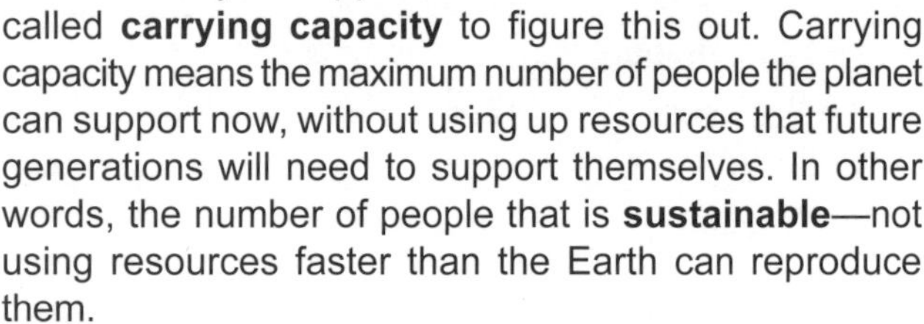

What's the Earth's Carrying Capacity?

This is a question on which experts disagree because carrying capacity depends on what kind of and how many resources are available. It also depends on how they are distributed and how much of them each person uses. Because different assumptions in each of those areas are used in estimating Earth's carrying capacity, these estimates range from as low as 1 billion people to as high as 44 billion people!

What we do know is that the Earth's carrying capacity can be limited by factors such as deforestation, soil erosion, and pollution. Higher levels of resource **consumption** per person can also reduce the Earth's carrying capacity.

Carrying capacity may be increased through technology. Fertilizers, hybrid seeds, and irrigation have increased food production. Modern transportation systems allow food to be moved across oceans, and low-cost energy has boosted industrial production tremendously.

What we also know is that some cultures have exceeded their local carrying capacity in the past. The Easter Island story in Chapter 1, *Sustainability*, shows one example of what can happen. Other cultures, when they get to the limit of their resources' carrying capacity, have responded differently, including immigrating and waging war with their neighbors. Like the Easter Islanders, however, Earth's human population currently doesn't have the option to emigrate somewhere new.

What's Your Shoe Size?

Because it's so difficult to determine the Earth's carrying capacity, some scientists have developed another way to study the impacts of human population and **lifestyles**. They use a concept called **ecological footprint**.

Each person has an ecological footprint, the area of the Earth's productive surface that it takes to support that person. This includes farmland, pasture, and fishing grounds to provide food, as well as forested area to provide lumber and paper. It takes into account lakes, rivers, and **aquifers** to provide freshwater. It includes all the area necessary to provide energy and jobs and dispose of wastes (including carbon dioxide). It also includes all the area needed to support the **infrastructure** of our lives, such as homes, highways, hospitals, schools, shopping malls, and baseball fields.

Ecological footprints vary tremendously with each person's lifestyle and resource consumption choices. Experts calculate that the average person in India has a footprint of less than 2 acres. By comparison, the average footprint is 6.4 acres in Mexico, 14 acres in France, and 23.6 acres in the United States.[35] Remember that this is an average and that some people in each of these countries have footprints that are bigger or smaller than that.

An acre is about the size of a football field. So now you can imagine the size of these people's average footprints and see the differences between them. If everyone on Earth had a footprint the size of the average U.S. citizen (24 football fields apiece), it would take five more planets, like Earth, to support us all![36]

As population grows, the total human footprint on Earth grows too. If the average level of resource consumption per person increases, the human footprint on Earth also increases. If both population and resource consumption per person increase—as is the case today—the total human footprint on Earth grows even faster.

A country's ecological footprint is the sum of its people's footprints, which depends on the number of people and their level of resource consumption. We saw in Chapter 3, Population Throughout History, that population is growing fastest in **developing countries**. Consumption, on the other hand, is greatest in **developed countries**. This means that while some rich countries have small populations, their total ecological footprint is greater than some poorer countries with much larger populations.

Today the average human footprint is estimated to be just over 5.5 acres. However, available ecological space on Earth is estimated to be 4.7 acres per person.[37] If these estimates are correct, that means that there is an **ecological deficit** because we are using resources more quickly than they can be renewed. That means we are living unsustainably and borrowing resources from future generations.

Reducing Humanity's Footprint

If the global human footprint is already larger than the Earth can support in the long run, what can we do about it?

One issue to look at is population. If more people means a bigger global footprint, then stabilizing our population is one way to limit our footprint on the planet. If we reduced world population over time, we would have even more resources available for each person.

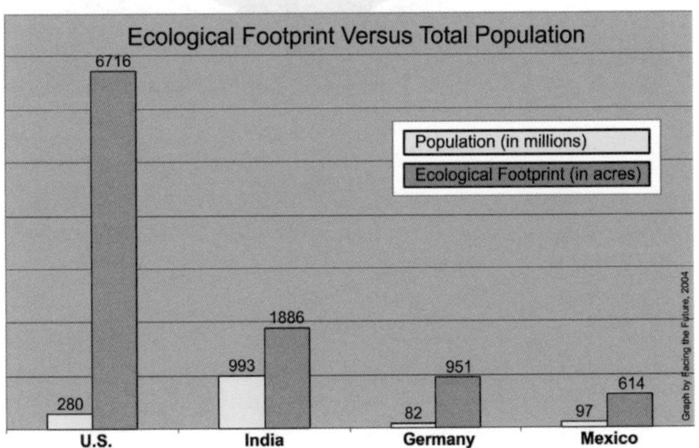

New technologies, like these windmills, can help us reduce our ecological footprint.

Another way to shrink our global footprint is through technology. Much of the human footprint today is taken up by the wastes we create, especially the land and water area needed to absorb our **carbon dioxide** emissions.[38] Since much of that carbon dioxide comes from burning oil and coal for energy, producing energy in new, nonpolluting ways can reduce our footprint significantly.

We can also shrink our footprint by reducing resource consumption. Some of this can be done by understanding what we truly need and consuming less. This means looking closely at how we live, including how much and what kind of food we eat, how we get around, what we do for recreation, and what we choose to buy. We can examine how much and what kind of energy we use. For example, switching to new technologies such as hybrid or fuel-cell cars and using solar-generated electricity can shrink our footprint. Finally, we need to examine whether the policies in our country and culture encourage sustainable or unsustainable consumption levels.

The challenge is that some people in the world desperately need to increase their consumption of resources. There are 1.2 billion people who live in **extreme poverty** around the world; they need more food, more education, more health care, and more fuel and energy resources. Only after their basic needs have been met and when they have economic options can these people make choices about sustainable consumption.

The good news is that there are some technologies—such as more effective farming techniques, wind-generated power, and cellular phones—that can help people consume more while not dramatically increasing their footprint. Yet poor people often can't afford to buy these technologies, so developed countries need to supply them and transport them to the places where they can be best used.

Ultimately, the number of people the Earth can support depends on the choices we make. Every day each of us makes decisions about our lifestyle, our economic system, our values, and what kind of world we want to live in. What kinds of choices can you make that will help the Earth maintain its carrying capacity?

Ecological Footprints

It's not only the number of footprints—size counts too. Let's compare the footprints of young people around the world: Bati in Kenya, Jyoti in India, and Warren in the United States.[39]

Bati Average Kenyan Footprint: 2.7 acres

In ***Kenya***, Bati gets up each day before dawn. He wears thin, patched shorts passed down from his two older brothers. Bati helps his mother start the wood fire to heat breakfast for him and his four siblings. His sisters fetch water from a stagnant river two miles away. Bati's whole family has a simple diet: Twice a day they eat green peas and corn boiled with a little bit of salt. Bati has tasted meat only a few times in his life.

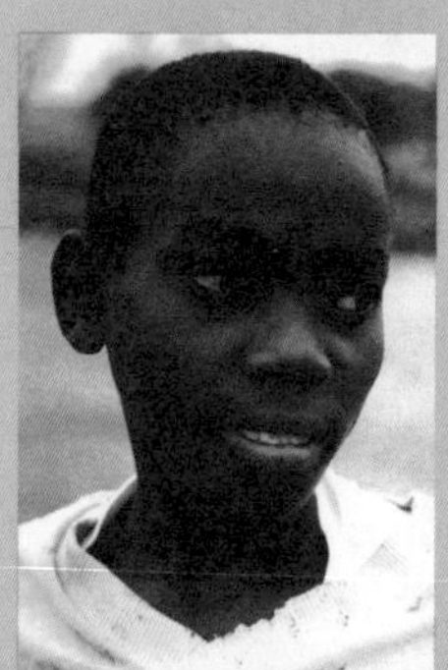

Photo by Devin Hibbard

Bati's house is made of mud bricks and a roof of wide leaves. The chickens sleep under the bed that he shares with his two brothers. His mother and two sisters sleep in the other room. Because his father works as a laborer in a town twelve hours away, Bati sees him only twice a year.

After breakfast, Bati goes out into his family's farm to pick peas and corn for the evening meal, and he takes the family's five chickens out to forage for food. Later he and his two best friends walk seven miles to gather wood for tonight's fire. They have to go farther every day because so many people are cutting trees for wood.

Photo by Devin Hibbard

Bati goes to school a few months of every year but is always behind because he misses classes so much. He would like to go to school to become a teacher or work in a store like his uncle does. However, his family can afford to send only the oldest son to high school. Bati knows he will probably be a farmer and raise his own family in this same area.

Bati had malaria last year, and everyone thought he would die. He was carried to the health clinic six hours away. He got medication and eventually got better, but now his mother can't buy the goat she was saving for because she spent the money on medicine.

Jyoti Average Indian Footprint: 1.9 acres

In ***India***, Jyoti lives in a mud house with her mother, father, two brothers, and sister. She gets up early and milks the cow. Breakfast is leftover rice and potato curry cooked over a clay stove using firewood as fuel. Each sister gets a few sips of milk, and Jyoti's brothers get a whole cup of milk each. Jyoti also has water to drink, which her mother draws every morning from the village well.

Photo by Devin Hibbard

After breakfast, Jyoti takes the cow out to the pasture, while her brothers change into their school uniforms and head to class. She wishes she could go to school too, but only a few of the girls in the village go. The reason Jyoti doesn't attend school isn't because her parents love her less; it's a question of money. In India, sons support the parents as they age, whereas daughters move out when they marry and help support their husband's family. For poor families in this situation, spending their few resources to educate sons makes more sense than educating their daughters.

Photo by Devin Hibbard

Jyoti has a busy day. She and her sisters work in the family's fields and then collect cow dung to be dried

Warren Average U.S. Citizen Footprint: 24 acres

On the other side of the world, in the ***United States***, Warren wakes up to his favorite CD he burned on the computer the night before. He puts on jeans that were made in Pennsylvania, a belt from Nebraska, a shirt made in Taiwan, socks from Massachusetts, and shoes that were produced and boxed in four different countries. His breakfast consists of eggs, bacon, toast, and orange juice. His mom will drive him to school in a car made in Japan and powered by gasoline from Saudi Arabia.

Warren has indoor plumbing, electricity, and a new video game that he likes to play. His parents are divorced and his dad works a lot, so Warren sees him about once a week.

At school, Warren is tired because he stayed up late playing video games. He gets pretty good grades, though, and his parents expect him to go to college. His dad wants him to be a doctor, but Warren would rather be a basketball star or a photographer for a nature magazine. After school, Warren and his friends ride their bikes to a place where they can spend their allowances on go-carts and video games, or they go to the skate park to practice skateboarding.

Warren visits the doctor and dentist every year, which he doesn't like at all. He is pretty healthy, but the dentist said he shouldn't eat so much junk food. His favorite foods are pizza and chocolate.

for fuel. In the afternoon when the sun is hot, Jyoti washes the family's clothes in a small bucket. Before dinner, she fetches the cow, gathers vegetables, and helps her mother prepare dinner. Her sisters fetch firewood in the forest thirty minutes away.

There is no electricity or running water in this village, so life is sometimes hard for Jyoti. She and all the other villagers use the fields around the village as their bathroom. When someone gets sick, they are taken by bicycle to the doctor. Only the richest family in the village can afford to hire a car to get to the doctor.

GLOBAL TRENDS FOOD, WATER, AND INCOME

Although there is debate about how many people the Earth can support, we can "grade" our progress in specific areas. This chapter looks at key resource **consumption** and availability trends in food, water, and income that help us figure out how we are doing.

Food for All?

As world population grows, we need to produce more and more food to feed everyone. Over the past fifty years, food production has kept pace with or grown faster than the rapidly growing population.

Part of the rapid increase in food production is due to the **green revolution**. Starting in the 1950s, scientists worked with farmers in **developing countries** to introduce fertilizers, pesticides, hybrid seeds, new machinery, and irrigation projects. This boosted the amount of food grown in each crop and resulted in more food than ever before.

Despite this increase in food production, today more than 840 million people—mostly women, children, and the elderly—are hungry.[40] This isn't because there's not enough food to go around. It's because food is not well distributed. People in the developed world consume much more food and calories than people in developing countries. In fact, the consumption of food is so out of balance that more than 1 billion people, mostly in **developed countries**, are now overnourished to the point of being overweight or obese.[41]

Harvesting wheat. Photo by USDA

Often poor people can't afford to buy the food they need and therefore they go hungry. Sometimes governments in poor countries export the food they grow in order to pay debts to other countries instead of using it to feed their people.

Some of the technologies of the green revolution, while they have increased food production and have fed many more people, also have had a high environmental impact. Some of the gains in food production came from creating more farmland by clearing forests, filling wetlands, and converting prairie land. These processes, however, have resulted in a loss of valuable habitats for people and animals. There isn't much more land that can readily be turned into farmland. In fact, because of population pressures, we are losing farmland each year to make way for houses, roads, and other forms of human development.

Intensive irrigation, which started during the green revolution, has also had a negative impact on the environment. Small amounts of salt and other minerals found in water build up in soil over time. Eventually, these saltier soils are not able to produce as much food. Also, pesticides and fertilizers sometimes run off fields and into lakes, rivers, and ground water, harming both animals and humans. Our challenge is continuing to grow enough food for everyone and finding technologies that are **sustainable**.

Fortunately, food production is projected to grow faster than population through 2030. However, experts believe that people will still go hungry in many parts of the world unless poverty and unequal food distribution systems are addressed.[42]

There are two big challenges to feeding the human population. The first is ensuring that the way we produce food is sustainable so that the systems that support all life on Earth are not damaged. Techniques that have been proven to protect the health of the soil and environment include planting a variety of crops, using beneficial insects to control crop pests, and growing crops that require less fertilizer and pesticides.[43]

The second challenge is ensuring that people can get the basic food they need and that our food distribution systems work so that no one is seriously malnourished or starving. It will take citizens and governments around the world working together to help people escape **extreme poverty** so that they can care for themselves and their families.[44]

Freshwater for Human Needs

Freshwater is just as important as food to human survival, but in many parts of the world, potable water is scarce.

That is because the Earth is able to produce only about the same amount of water from year to year. Humans can't make very much more, and the Earth just recycles

Guatemalan women carrying water. Photo by Water Partners International

the water that we already have. This means that as population grows, the available water per person decreases.

Currently, more than 1 billion people lack access to freshwater, and more than 3 million people die every year from diseases related to unclean water.[45]

One major source of freshwater is aquifers, underground lakes that wells tap. Some aquifers get recharged by rainwater draining into the ground. Others, called fossil aquifers, recharge extremely slowly, over millions of years, if at all. Once they're pumped dry, the stored water is gone forever.

For example, after years of being used for farming, the Ogallala Aquifer in the United States has fallen sharply in some areas and run completely dry in others. As a result, farmers in parts of the Great Plains of the United States have faced water shortages. Some farmers have been forced to stop irrigating their land altogether.

Rivers, another important source of freshwater for drinking, are being diverted for other uses, such as dams for producing electricity and water for irrigation. Great rivers such as the Nile in Africa, the Ganges in India, the Huang He in China, and the Colorado in the United States sometimes run dry before reaching the sea. Some communities have prospered from these projects but others haven't, and some of the plants, animals, and fish that depended on these rivers have disappeared.

Rivers and aquifers are both fed by rain and snowfall. Climate changes can cause weather patterns to shift, which sometimes means that rain or snow falls less or in different places. Snow is particularly important because it stores the water over time, gradually releasing it as the snow melts. Some experts believe that the current trend in **global warming** is already reducing the amount of

Fishing for the Future[46]

A key food source in the world today is fish. One billion people rely on fish as their primary source of animal protein[47], and 60 percent of all people live within 200 kilometers of a seacoast. Around the world, 200 million people depend on fishing for their livelihood.

Unfortunately, today 70 percent of all fish and seafood that people depend on are being fished to capacity or overfished, which means that the remaining fish cannot continue to produce high levels for harvest. In many places, such as the East Coast of the United States, some stocks of fish are so low that the fishing industry that depends on those stocks is threatened. One model of a more sustainable fishery is the Alaskan ground-fish fishery, which produces half of all U.S. fish production and where no fisheries are overfished.

Alaska Fishery. Photo by Marine Conservation Alliance

Although the number of fish is declining, demand for fish is increasing as the population grows. By 2010, an additional 15.5 million tons of fish will be required just to maintain the current rates of fish consumption around the world. To meet this need, more fish are being grown in farms. Experts believe that some fish farms can cause environmental damage or that farmed fish, when they escape, can threaten existing stocks of wild fish. However, fish farms are also an important step to producing the protein needed to feed the growing population.

Part of the difficulty is that many countries do not manage their fisheries sustainably, allowing fishermen to catch as much fish as they can. As one fishery is overfished, fishermen shift to harvesting another species and continue to repeat the pattern until many stocks are diminished.

Individuals can play a role in creating sustainable fisheries. Learning about the fish that are most overfished, such as swordfish, Chilean sea bass, and bluefin tuna, and not purchasing those fish until the stocks have recovered are ways that consumers can help save fisheries.

For a full list of the fish that are endangered and those that are the best choices for consumers, go to www.mbayaq.org/cr/seafoodwatch.asp.

snow accumulating in some mountains.[48] In the past, water shortages have forced civilizations to move or sometimes to collapse.

Sorting Mangoes in Guinea. Photo from UN FAO

Currently, twenty-five countries representing more than 600 million people face water scarcity, which means they can't get enough water throughout the year to meet their needs.[49] Many of these countries are also experiencing rapid population growth.

Water scarcity in many parts of the world has led to predictions that in this century, wars will be fought over who has access to water.[50]

Fortunately, there are many ways we can conserve water. Seventy percent of all freshwater is used for growing food and raising crops. Factories and industry use another 22 percent, and 8 percent is used directly by people for drinking, bathing, and other household use.[51]

Because agriculture requires a large amount of freshwater, one way to conserve water is to irrigate crops more efficiently. Researchers have found that there are many ways to grow the same amount of food while using less water for irrigation. Technologies such as drip irrigation and irrigating less often but with more precise timing can save up to 25 percent of the water used to grow crops.[52]

Another key to water conservation is growing food that requires less water to produce. For example, it takes about 37 times more water to raise 500 calories' worth of beef than it does to grow corn that provides the same amount of calories. (It takes more than 12,000 gallons of water to create a hamburger that provides 500 calories.)[53] If people around the world eat a diet that requires less water to produce, there will be more water left for other essential needs.

The other important step is distributing water to the people who need it. Some countries have more than enough water, while others don't have enough. The challenge is both to conserve the water we currently use and to make sure everyone has access to the water they need.

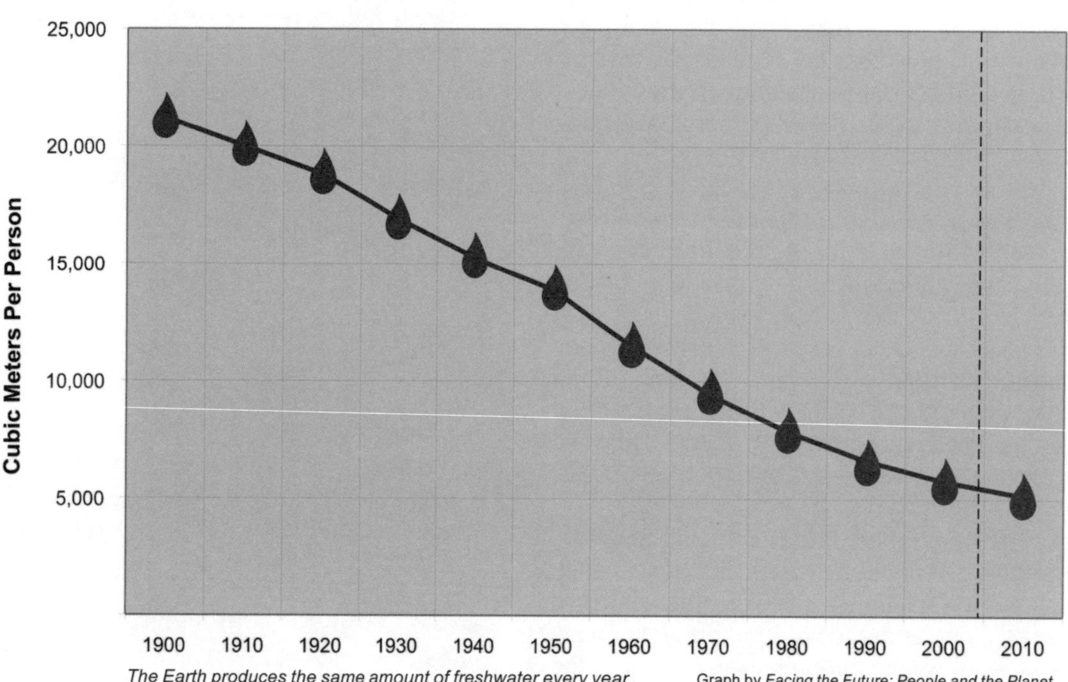

The Earth produces the same amount of freshwater every year. Graph by *Facing the Future: People and the Planet*

Economic Inequity—Where's the Money?

As the world becomes more and more urban, the most essential resource for most people is income: money with which to purchase essentials such as food, water, and energy. Like food and water, money is also unevenly distributed. Two out of every five people on the planet—2.8 billion people—live on less than $2 a day, and 1.2 billion live on less than $1 a day.[54]

Since 1960, the gap between rich and poor countries has grown steadily. Today:

- The twenty richest countries have thirty-seven times the **gross domestic product** (GDP) of the twenty poorest countries.[55]
- The richest 1 percent of the global population receives as much income as the poorest 57 percent.[56]
- The wealth of the world's 200 richest people equals the combined annual income of the world's poorest 2.5 billion people.[57]

This inequality exists not only on a global scale, but within countries as well. In the United States, the richest 10 percent of the population earns more than 30 percent of national income, while the poorest 10 percent earns only 1.8 percent. Among all high-income nations, the United States has the most unequal distribution of income between rich and poor people. However, other countries also have rising inequality. The policies and patterns of forty-eight other countries around the world caused their economic inequality to increase between 1980 and 2000.[58]

There are many reasons for inequitable distribution of wealth. One is that colonization resulted in many resources from developing countries being taken and used by developed countries. This extraction of resources left little opportunities for wealth and **infrastructure**, such as water and sewer facilities, schools, hospitals, and roads. Experts also point to existing trade and economic policies that put developing countries at a disadvantage. **Globalization** can increase these trends if people don't have an education that allows them to compete in a global economy.[59]

People in extreme poverty have few opportunities to escape poverty or to participate in the global economy. A majority of those in poverty are women, reflecting the fact that around the world, women have less access to power, money, and political decision making.[60]

While income will likely never be equally distributed, a large gap between the rich and the poor has costs for people as well as the planet. Because rich people can pay for what they want, these things are often produced, while products that poor people need for basic survival

You Do the Math [64]

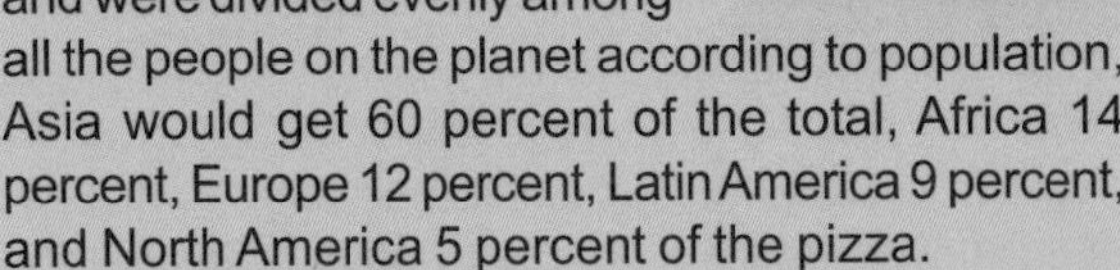

Dividing up the world's resources...

If world resources were a pizza and were divided evenly among all the people on the planet according to population, Asia would get 60 percent of the total, Africa 14 percent, Europe 12 percent, Latin America 9 percent, and North America 5 percent of the pizza.

However, resources aren't divided equally. If the pizza were divided by **gross national income** (GNI) adjusted for **purchasing power parity** (PPP), North America would have 24 percent of the total, Europe would have 27 percent, Latin America 8 percent, Asia 37 percent, and Africa 4 percent.

Who Has the Most People?

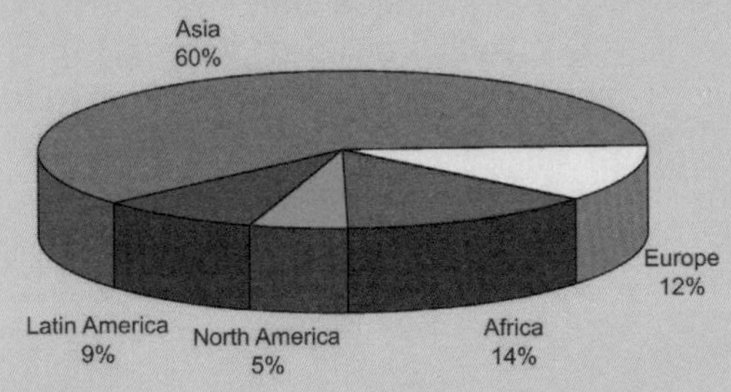

Who Has the Most Money?

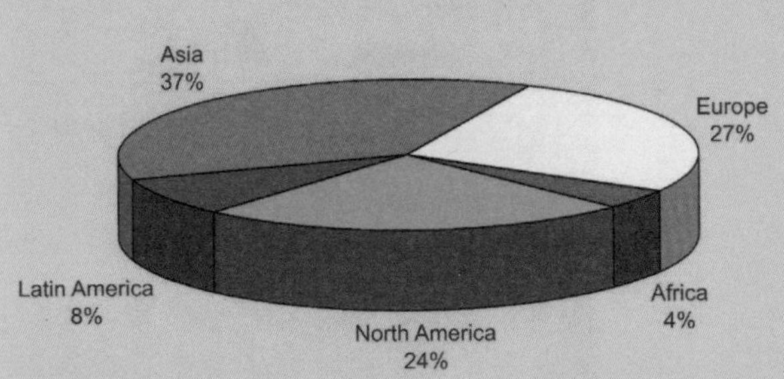

These graphs use data on population and gross national income adjusted for PPP. GNI measures the total income of a country's residents. PPP means that different currencies can be compared to each other in terms of how much they buy. So if someone in India has a GNI PPP of $2,820, that means they could buy items in India equal in value to what you could buy with $2,820 in the U.S.

are sometimes not produced because poor people can't afford to buy them. When poor people can't afford to buy necessities, they often make do by having larger families, taking resources directly from their environment, or migrating to support themselves.

At the same time, people with large **ecological footprints** also have a big impact on the planet because of their high consumption levels, which take additional resources from the environment. This consumer class exists around the world, with wealthy people living in both developed and developing countries.

Evidence shows that an increasing income has a strong effect on increasing a person's health and happiness, but only up to a certain level. Once people achieve basic economic security, additional money doesn't have a significant effect on increasing people's happiness.[61]

Global Trends, Human Choices

While it's easy to get discouraged over all of these serious trends, it's also important to understand that these are only the directions our world is going at this time. Human choices created these conditions, and we can make new choices to change them. Understanding these challenges helps us develop better, more sustainable solutions.

For example, as recently as 1950 to 1970, in many countries the gap between rich and poor decreased.[62] If inequality decreased forty years ago, it can be addressed again. However, just because it is possible to do doesn't mean it is easy to do. Experts note that there is broad agreement on policies that can reduce extreme poverty and that what is missing is the political will to meet the challenge.[63]

Many available technologies help promote sustainable food production, some of which are already being used. Also, ways to conserve water can allow us to use less water per person so that we can accommodate our growing population.

With both food and water, the challenge is making sure that the very poorest people have access to both. Growing enough food to feed every person on the planet doesn't help if the food doesn't get to the people who are hungry.

By taking actions to help meet these challenges and giving people informed choices, we can begin to turn these trends around and help create sustainable communities for all people.

Carrying water in Ethiopia. Photo by UN FAO

ENVIRONMENTAL SUSTAINABILITY

Our environment produces everything that human beings need to survive. All of our food, clothing, schools, and even computers have materials that come from the planet in one way or another. It is important to understand not only how we use these resources, but also the ability of the environment to supply them over the long term.

Sometimes it takes resources a long time to recover, whereas sometimes they don't recover at all. Many environmental trends show that we are having a greater and greater impact on the planet. For example:

- Half of the planet's tropical rain forests have been destroyed or degraded.[65]
- Human activities are linked to warmer temperatures around the world.[66]
- On average, every hour three unique plant and animal species become extinct.[67]
- Overall, all of the world's ecosystems are shrinking to make way for humans.[68]

There are two main causes of negative environmental trends: our rapidly expanding population and **ecological footprints** that are larger than the Earth can sustain.[69]

The Function of Forests

Humans are now using up forests faster and in more places than ever before. Less than one hundred years ago, forests covered about 40 percent of the Earth's land surface. Today we have lost almost half of that forest, and an additional 40 million acres are cut down each year.[70]

Why is that a problem? For one thing, forests are habitat for millions of animal, plant, and insect species. When the forests disappear, so do those species.

Sustainably-managed forestland in Lakeview, Oregon.
Photo courtesy of Collins Companies

Forests also release oxygen and take in **carbon dioxide**, which helps regulate our atmosphere. Scientists call forests "carbon sinks" because they capture carbon dioxide and keep it out of the atmosphere. For example, forests in the United States remove approximately 25 percent of total carbon dioxide emissions yearly.[71] This is important because too much carbon dioxide in the atmosphere can contribute to **global warming** and climate change. When forests are removed and replaced with nonforest uses, they no longer provide oxygen for the planet or capture additional carbon dioxide.

Preventing erosion is another important function of forests. When all the trees are cut from a mountainside, there is a higher chance of erosion, which can cause mudslides and flooding.

Scientists say that deforestation is linked to disastrous flooding in India, China, and Honduras. The effects of flooding are more severe as more and more people are forced to move into floodplains when they can't find anywhere else to live because of crowding in surrounding areas.

Increased population and the resulting increased **consumption** of resources are main reasons why forests are cut down. Clearing forest for farmland to produce more food is a big cause of deforestation in **developing countries**. Harvesting wood for fuel in those countries is another cause. In southern Africa, for example, 80 percent of the population uses wood to cook their food and heat their homes.[72]

Another reason why forests are cut down is that richer countries use a large amount of wood. People from Europe, the United States, and Japan, who make up less than 20 percent of the world's population, use more than 50 percent of the world's timber and more than 66 percent of its paper.[73] They use a great deal of wood for construction of homes. This is partly because the population is growing and partly because homes in these places are almost twice the size they were fifty years ago.

If population trends continue, deforestation is likely to get worse. Nearly all of the expected population growth will likely happen in poorer countries, where poverty and lack of access to land mean that people will clear the forests for farming. Cutting forests for use in **developed countries** will continue, too, if more people continue to consume at a high level and have large ecological footprints.

In some urban areas, wood fuel is sold and bought on the market, as is done by these girls in Burkina Faso.
Photo by Saskia Everts/TOOL Consult, courtesy of Photoshare

Because trees and forests grow back, they can be a **sustainable** resource. The challenge is that when forests are cut often and not allowed to grow back, they can no longer stop erosion or provide animal habitat. One form of sustainable forestry is **selective harvesting**, in which only a portion of the forest is cut each year. This leaves many trees standing, so that the forest is still intact and can provide habitat, recreation space, and conversion of carbon dioxide into oxygen.

Sustainable tree harvesting can be more costly to do, and the volume of trees harvested in a single cut is lower than in conventional logging. However, studies have shown that selective harvesting does less damage to the forested area and retains more soil nutrients, promoting better growth of the remaining trees. Experts believe the cost of sustainable harvesting will drop in the future and note that from ecological, economic, and social perspectives, selective logging creates a more sustainable, high-quality timber supply.[74]

Technologies and alternative approaches also could dramatically reduce the number of trees cut down in **developing countries** each year. One example is a simple technology called a smokeless Chula, a small stove built with an aluminum stovepipe and clay. The stove burns more efficiently by channeling the heat toward the cooking pot, rather than letting most of the heat escape to the sides as it does in an open fire. The smokeless Chula requires two-thirds less wood to cook the same meal, reducing the amount of wood people need for cooking. It also channels smoke out of the cooking space, reducing illness in women and girls who inhale the smoke. The total cost of installing a smokeless Chula in India is around $9 (U.S.).[75]

Other technologies and decisions that would reduce the consumption of forests by rich nations include using different materials (such as bamboo, clay, or plastic that looks like wood) for construction and using paper products made from recycled paper. People can also use less wood by building smaller houses and using scrap or reclaimed lumber when possible.

Biodiversity

Each year as many as 27,000 species of animals, plants, insects, or microorganisms vanish forever.[76] Mountain gorillas, giant pandas, and snow leopards are among several animal species on the brink of extinction. Many scientists believe that between 20 percent and 50 percent of all species on Earth could disappear in the next thirty years.[77]

The main threat to this variety of species, what scientists call **biodiversity**, is habitat loss caused by human activities. When forests are cut down or wetlands are drained for agriculture or construction, the plants and animals that live there often can't survive.

Why should you care about the disappearance of animals, plants, or insects you've probably never even seen? The essentials all of us need to live—clean air, pure water, healthy crops—all depend on the web of life being kept intact. When we take any species out of the web, we remove a strand that helps hold our own lives together. For example, scientists estimate that 70 percent of the drugs used in modern medicine are modeled after natural compounds found in nature. One estimate says that we have tested less than 1 percent of the plants that are likely to help us find additional medicines.[78] If we allow species to become extinct, we may limit the resources we have to treat disease or illnesses now and in the future.

Endangered Snow Leopard. Photo by Dennis Conner, courtesy of International Snow Leopard Trust

In addition, the habitats that other species depend on often provide humans with important needs, too; for example, wetlands clean pollutants out of the water people drink and forests release oxygen humans breathe and provide wilderness for recreation.

Tragedy of the Commons[79]

Photo by USDA

Imagine that you live in a small town where everyone raises sheep. Outside of the town is a meadow where people graze their sheep. The meadow is just big enough to support ten sheep, and for as long as you can remember, ten families lived around the village. Each family grazed one sheep on the common land.

Your neighbor, however, decides that since grazing in the meadow is free, she will get one more sheep and graze it in the meadow too. Now there are eleven sheep grazing in the meadow, and your neighbor is now making more money selling the wool. You and some of your other neighbors decide to do the same thing; after all, it's free.

After a couple of seasons of grazing by these new sheep, there isn't enough grass for all the sheep and, because they are hungry, they nibble the grass down to the roots. The meadow becomes a big mud patch, and eventually the sheep die, affecting all the families in the village.

This concept is called the **Tragedy of the Commons**. It shows what can happen when a resource is owned in common and yet not managed in common. Because the resource is free, your neighbor wants to take a little bit more of it so she can get ahead. Eventually, however, the resource is used up and can't produce for anyone.

The Tragedy of the Commons is seen in many instances. The atmosphere is a commons because it doesn't belong to anyone and it crosses national borders. Some countries may have an industry that creates a great deal of pollution, which is absorbed by the air and carried across many regions. It is cheaper for any one country if it doesn't have to control the pollution it creates, but that pollution has an effect on everyone's air quality. The good news is that with careful management, we can avoid the tragedy that happened to the meadow in this story.

Many people are concerned about species extinction, and governments have even passed laws to protect animals in danger of becoming extinct. Many animals that were once considered endangered are now protected by laws such as the U.S. Endangered Species Act (ESA), and their populations are rebuilding. However, many other species may become extinct because scientists don't have enough data on them or existing laws haven't yet protected them.

The bald eagle is one animal species that was once endangered but now has a healthy population size. The bald eagle was protected by the ESA in 1967 when scientists counted fewer than 450 nesting pairs of eagles in the continental United States. The government also acted to ban DDT, a farming pesticide that often ran into streams and contaminated fish that were then eaten by bald eagles. There are now more than 5,000 nesting pairs of bald eagles, and in 1999 the U.S. Fish and Wildlife Service recommended taking bald eagles off the endangered species list.[80]

A Breath of Fresh Air

Human activities often pollute the Earth's atmosphere, causing smog, acid rain, damage to the ozone layer, and contributions to global warming. Emissions from cars and industrial factories are the major culprit.

Worldwide, more than 600 million cars and trucks are in use today, and nearly 50 million new ones are added each year.[81] Almost all cars burn gasoline or other fossil fuels that cause air pollution.

Chorus Frog (formerly Pacific Tree Frog) Photo by Paul Bannick

Many governments have air pollution standards that limit industrial pollution in order to protect the health of citizens. For example, the state of California has passed automobile pollution laws that permit less pollution than is allowed by nationwide standards. These regulations have led to better air quality in many places.[82]

However, government regulations are not always enforced, and in many places air pollution has become a serious concern. In Mexico City, smog is so thick on some days that schools and factories close and cars have to drive with their lights on. Pollution has an economic cost when it causes sickness and keeps people home from work. Researchers in Mexico City estimate that reducing two of the most serious air pollutants by 10 percent would save an average of $760 million a year.[83]

Scientists also believe that pollution can contribute to asthma, which continues to increase by 50 percent worldwide every decade.[84] In the United States, 17.3 million people have asthma—more than double the rate just fifteen years ago. Every day, an average of fifteen U.S. citizens die from asthma.[85] It is estimated that asthma costs U.S. society more than $11 billion a year.[86]

Scientists have identified two important problems in the atmosphere: holes in the ozone layer and global warming. **Ozone holes** are caused by specific pollutants that escape into the atmosphere and weaken the ozone layer. This is a challenge because the ozone layer filters out harmful ultraviolet rays from the sun. Think of the ozone layer as the Earth's sunscreen. When the ozone gets "holes" in it, too much ultraviolet light gets through and can cause skin cancer and crop damage.

The good news is that the international community has responded to the danger of ozone holes by taking a range of actions. Because of international treaties, the production of chemicals that harm the ozone has fallen sharply. If these trends continue, scientists predict that the ozone holes will begin shrinking in the next decade and be fully recovered by 2050.[87]

Global warming is another danger to our atmosphere. Global warming happens when certain gasses, such as carbon dioxide, build up in the atmosphere and entrap heat from the sun. This can raise the temperature of the Earth's climate. Burning fossil fuels such as coal, oil, and natural gas is the main way that these harmful **greenhouse gases** are created.

Because of government protection under the U.S. Endangered Species Act, there are now more than 5,000 nesting pairs of bald eagles. Photo by Paul Bannick

All over the world, temperatures are rising—the ten warmest years on record have occurred since 1980.[88] Although scientists have shown that the Earth's temperatures have varied over hundreds of thousands of years, most scientists agree that human activity is a major cause of the current warming trend.[89]

Global warming can create many challenges. Sea levels are slowly rising as the warmer temperatures melt the polar icecaps, flooding some low-lying areas.[90] Heat waves, hurricanes, droughts, and flooding are all thought to be related to increasing temperatures. Cyclic warming of ocean currents in the Pacific, a phenomenon called "El Niño," has caused periodic declines in populations of Pacific salmon and a temporary shift in the distribution of some marine fish species.[91]

Currently, people living in rich countries create 60 percent of all carbon dioxide emissions.[92] However, since most future population growth will occur in developing countries, energy demand is likely to increase there. Also, as people in developing countries improve their standard of living, they will create more carbon dioxide emissions if they depend on traditional technologies such as the gasoline-powered internal combustion engine.

African Elephants. Photo by Charles Steinberg

One hopeful sign is that many governments have taken action on global warming with international agreements such as the **Kyoto Protocol**, which requires countries to reduce the greenhouse gases they produce. However, not all

Youth working for environmental justice. Photo courtesy of Greenaction

countries (including the United States) have signed on to the accord.

Also, many technologies can be used that create less pollution. For example, hybrid, bio-diesel, and fuel cell cars use much less gasoline and create less carbon dioxide. Solar panels use the sun's energy to create electricity and power with no harmful pollution. The opportunity to use more of these technologies—especially in places where many people don't yet have cars or electricity—can leapfrog over the polluting technologies of developed countries and allow people to raise their standard of living without expanding their ecological footprint by very much.

Environmental Justice

The environment is not just remote forests or untouched wilderness. It is also the backyards, the neighborhood parks, and the communities in which we live in. Many projects and activities that damage the environment take place closer to the homes of poor or minority people than they do to the homes of people who have more resources or power. For example, facilities to treat toxic waste, garbage incinerators, and factories that create pollution are often located in poorer communities.

Studies in the United States have found that low-income and African-American children consistently have higher rates of asthma and traces of lead than other children. In addition, 80 percent of Hispanic and 65 percent of African-American people, compared to only 57 percent of white people, live in communities that fail to meet some government air quality standards[93].

People who are concerned about these trends are working to ensure **environmental justice** for all people. They want to make sure that projects that negatively impact the environment or people's health are distributed throughout society and don't affect one group more than another.

What Can We Do?

Projections show that there will be almost 3 billion more people on the planet during the next thirty to forty years.[94] These people will all want a good standard of living for themselves and their families. We have to figure out how to make sure people get the resources they need without compromising the capacity of the Earth to generate more resources in the future.

The good news is that we can protect the natural world and still meet human needs. To do that, we must establish conditions that allow all people to make sustainable choices.

That means addressing population growth and maybe even reversing it. It will require addressing **extreme poverty**, which causes so many people to use the environment in unsustainable ways to survive. Developing and using more renewable, nonpolluting energy sources is another key, as is developing technologies and ways of doing business that don't use more resources than the Earth can provide.

This reality is within our reach. We have the technology, the knowledge, and the money to do what is necessary. We need a vision of a positive, secure, and healthy future, and we'll need to work together to make it happen.

New technology such as this car that runs on bio-diesel (vegetable oil) can help create a more sustainable world. Photo courtesy of Bio-Beetle

PEOPLE AND THE PLANET
WHAT IS THE GOOD LIFE?

Achieving **sustainability** requires that we look not only at the state of the environment but also at how people around the world are doing. In the preceding chapters, we have seen how population growth, poverty, and resource **consumption** affect the environment. It is sometimes harder to see how these are connected to social and economic issues. At first glance, disease, migration, and unemployment might not seem to have much to do with sustainability.

In fact, the health and well-being of people is connected to the health and well-being of the planet. To create a sustainable future, we need to understand the challenges facing people around the world and explore ways that we can help meet these challenges.

Poverty and Jobs

Whether or not people are able to meet their basic needs affects their environmental impact, their family size, and the choices they can make about resource consumption.

Because of poverty, housing shortages, and lack of jobs, millions of people around the world live in and around garbage pits. Like these children at the dump in Recife, Brazil, they survive by scavenging food and items to sell from the trash. Photo from UN FAO

Unfortunately, poverty is increasing around the world. While the percentage of people living in poverty is getting smaller, the number of poor people is rising—because of population growth.[95] In the developing world, 1.2 billion people live on less than $1 a day,[96] and 840 million of these don't get enough food to meet their basic daily needs.[97]

Some poor people are forced to overuse the environment to meet their needs. People struggling to survive are responsible for some of the overgrazing, deforestation, and soil depletion that damages ecosystems around the world.[98]

Brick hauler in Peru: For poor families, having lots of children makes economic sense. Kids help support their families by producing food, hauling water, begging on the street, or hiring out to sweatshops. Photo by John Goekler

Poverty is also linked to population growth because having more children often helps a poor family survive. In poor countries, children may help with the essential jobs of growing and gathering food, hauling water, and collecting firewood. Some children work in sweatshops or beg on the streets. Girls are sometimes sold into slavery or prostitution as the only way a family can survive. As grim as it may seem, in these harsh conditions having more children helps a family survive.

The contributions of children change as people move out of **extreme poverty**. Often the first thing a family does when it isn't struggling for daily survival is to send one or more children to school. Parents know an education can help the child and the entire family in the future. Families with more money may pay for their children to attend better schools or even save for their children to attend college. As the cost of raising children increases, families tend to have a few well-educated children rather than to have a larger number of children who aren't able to attend school.[99]

In order to make a transition to a higher income level, people around the world look for opportunities. Everywhere around the world, most people would prefer to work hard to support themselves and their families rather than receive a handout from someone else.

Unfortunately, while world population has more than doubled in the last forty years, jobs have not been created at the same pace. The International Labor Organization estimates that 730 million people worldwide are unemployed or underemployed.[100] This means that people are forced to survive as best they can without a job or a steady income. As technology replaces jobs in private companies, perhaps communities will need to pay people to work in social jobs, such as teachers, coaches, caregivers, and artists.

Healthy People

Being healthy is something that everyone around the world cares about. People want their families to be healthy and survive. Advances in medicine in the past fifty years have meant that more people around the world are surviving past childhood and that the average life span is increasing. In fact, this has been one of the major reasons for population growth during this time.

However, humans are currently encountering new diseases. Since 1970, at least thirty-five previously unknown diseases have been identified, including Acquired Immuno-Deficiency Syndrome (AIDS), Ebola Virus, Sudden Acute Respiratory Syndrome (SARS), and West Nile Virus.[101] At the same time, twenty well-known diseases, including tuberculosis, malaria, and cholera, have reemerged or spread to new areas.[102]

The emergence of new diseases is due mostly to human activity as people cultivate new land areas and engage in intensive farming practices, creating and spreading disease from animals to humans.[103] Because our transportation system has made it easier for people to travel around the world, it's also easier for new diseases to spread quickly over larger areas. Increasing global temperatures also allow pests and diseases to survive in places where they never could in the past.

Larger human populations and poverty can also make those diseases harder to cure. Sick people need doctors, clinics, and medical supplies, but in many **developing countries**, the government can't or won't provide all of these services, and people may be too poor to afford health care. Every year, 4 million children around the world die from disease because their families can't afford the vaccines.[104]

People on the Move

All around the world, people are on the move, and often it is to the cities. Today one-half of the world's population lives in cities.[105] Often people move from rural to urban areas in search of better economic opportunities. This will continue as the rural population grows, farm jobs disappear, the environment is degraded, and people seek economic opportunities that exist in cities. Even those who move to cities, however, are often desperately poor

AIDS in Africa

Seventeen million people in Africa have died of HIV/AIDS, and an additional 30 million people are infected with the Human Immunodeficiency Virus (HIV).[106]

In many countries in sub-Saharan Africa, more than 25 percent of the population is infected with HIV. In Botswana, one out of every three adults has HIV and is expected to die by 2010. Because of this, projected life expectancy in Botswana has fallen from seventy-one years to thirty-nine years.[107]

AIDS strikes people who are productive workers in society. It also hits more women than men. In South Africa, one of every five girls of age fifteen to nineteen is HIV-positive.[108] By 2010, Africa is expected to have almost 25 million AIDS orphans.[109]

Losing so many productive members of society hurts education, food production, and the economy. A study estimated that South Africa's economy is expected to be 17 percent lower in 2010 than it would have been without AIDS.[110] The epidemic is so widespread that the U.S. Central Intelligence Agency (CIA) has called it a potential national security threat because the loss of so many adults could lead to social and political instability.[111]

AIDS accounts for almost one-third of the slowing global population growth rate. In spite of the AIDS epidemic, however, the total population of sub-Saharan Africa is still expected to increase by nearly 140 percent from 2000 to 2050 due to high fertility rates.[112]

Adolescents work on an AIDS mural at the University of Durban in Westville, South Africa as part of the Beyond Awareness Campaign.
Photo by Gary Lewis/CCP, courtesy of Photoshare

and live in slums with no sewage systems or clean drinking water.[113]

Another group of people on the move are those who migrate from one country to another. About 175 million people—3 percent of the human population—around the world are international migrants; this means they don't live in the country in which they were born.[114] Generally, people who move to another country are classified as either **immigrants** or **refugees**.

Immigrants are people who move for economic or personal reasons. Some people immigrate to a new country legally, others illegally. When we think about immigration, it is helpful to understand both the "push" factors that exist in the home country as well as the "pull" factors that draw someone to a new country. Commonly, lack of jobs, land, food, and other resources are what push immigrants to make the difficult decision to leave their home.

Two Kinds of Scarcity

Scarcity is a big piece of the sustainability puzzle. When there aren't enough resources to go around, people may fall into poverty. They may discriminate against others and deny them resources. They may move somewhere else to find resources. Or they may fight to control scarce resources.

There are two kinds of scarcity: environmental and structural. **Environmental scarcity** means there just isn't enough to go around. Imagine, for example, that someone brought a big cheese pizza for your class, a pizza big enough for everyone to get a large slice. Now imagine inviting three more classes in to share the pizza. Everyone will get only a tiny piece. That's environmental scarcity, and it is often caused by too many people or too few resources in a given area.

Structural scarcity means that the resources aren't fairly shared: someone gets a large amount and most people get only a little. Imagine that same pizza in your classroom. Everyone wants some, but instead of dividing it equally, the teacher decides the tallest person gets half the pizza. The next tallest gets a quarter of the pizza, the next tallest gets an eighth, and everyone else has to share what's left. That's structural scarcity; it is based on policies and practices that people set up, often on the basis of political and economic power.

Both kinds of scarcity contribute to environmental damage as well as social and political unrest.

Girls practice writing at the Kakuma Refugee Camp in Kenya.
Photo by Kathryn Wolford/Lutheran World Relief, courtesy of Photoshare

The possibility of a job, political freedom, high wages, and a higher standard of living are what pulls people to move somewhere new. One study found that immigrants from Mexico earned $31 a week in their last job in Mexico, compared to $278 a week in the United States.[115] This difference makes it easier to understand why people immigrate.

It is estimated that each year there are 120 million immigrants worldwide.[116] People generally move from countries with quickly growing populations in Africa, Latin America, and Asia. They most often go to western Europe, North America, or Australia.

The other group of people who are leaving their countries are refugees. These are people who leave their homes out of the fear that they will be discriminated against because of their race, religion, nationality, or political beliefs. Fifteen million people are officially classified as refugees, and the United Nations considers another 12 million people vulnerable to becoming refugees.[117]

Internally displaced people are those forced to leave their homes because of war, food scarcity, or other crisis but who remain within their country. Around the world, 52 million people in more than fifty countries fall into this category.[118] Both refugees and internally displaced people are more vulnerable to sickness, violence, and discrimination.

Many countries debate how much immigration they should allow. Some argue that immigrants, who are generally poor, are taking jobs and benefits from legal citizens. There have even been violent attacks against immigrants in many countries around the world. Others note that immigrants generally contribute more to the society than they take, and they often fill jobs that no one else will do.

None for YOU Girl!

When there aren't enough resources to go around, somebody gets less. And whether the resource is food, education, income, or credit, it's most often girls and women who get less:

* Of the 1.2 billion people in extreme poverty, 70 percent are female.[119]
* Two of every three illiterate people in the world are female.[120]
* Around the world, women hold only 11 percent of the seats in parliaments or equivalent elected positions.[121]
* Four million women or more have been taken from their own countries and forced to become prostitutes, slave laborers, or mail-order brides. Trafficking of women is estimated to generate $5 billion to $7 billion every year.[122]

Reversing this trend—supporting equal rights for women and investing in women's education—is essential for sustainable development.

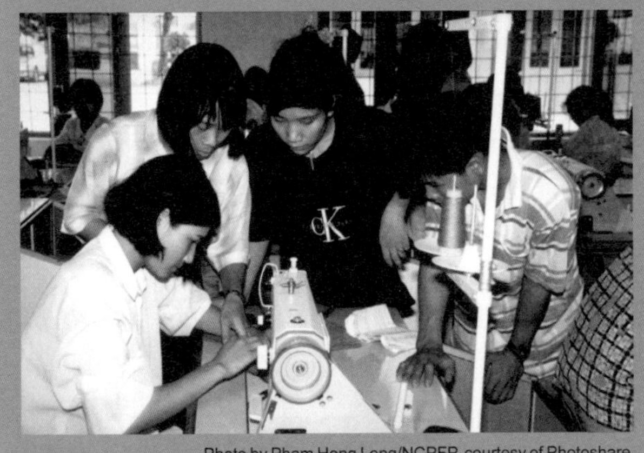

Photo by Pham Hong Long/NCPFP, courtesy of Photoshare

Peace and Conflict

There are many causes of conflict between or within countries, but economic inequality, ethnic disputes, pressure on scarce resources, poverty, and population pressures are all factors that can contribute to these conflicts.[123] Resource scarcity was linked to conflicts in Rwanda, Somalia, and Chiapas, Mexico.[124]

Control of scarce drinking water is one issue contributing to the ongoing conflict between the Israelis and Palestinians. Israel controls most of the water in the region, and Palestinians face frequent water scarcity.[125]

Poverty, poor health, low levels of education, disease, and a lack of economic opportunities can also breed hopelessness, which in some cases can create fertile ground for terrorism.[126]

Conflicts often results in mass migrations as refugees flee war and try to find a safe place for themselves and their families. Such migrations can create environmental damage as people cut and burn firewood and hunt wild animals in an effort to survive.[127]

Finally, beyond the tremendous costs in human life and suffering, conflicts have financial costs. The economic impacts of conflicts linger for years, when **infrastructure** or farmlands that people depend on for jobs are destroyed. **Developed countries** also spend money to end conflicts. Experts estimate that international conflict intervention in the 1990s cost $230 billion and that earlier intervention would have saved almost $130 billion.[128] Balancing security costs with sustainable development is a challenge.

What Can We Do?

Although some solutions are complicated, there are things we can do about all the social issues discussed in this chapter. Remember the global issues mobile discussed in Chapter 1, *Sustainability*? Because these issues are interconnected, so are the solutions, which can magnify their success. Efforts to provide reproductive and community health care, fight poverty, expand education, increase jobs, or protect the environment all help promote each other. For example, when a girl gets an education, she generally will have a smaller family when she grows up, and her family will be less likely to be impoverished.[129]

As individuals, we can learn more about these important **quality of life** issues, talk to our friends and family about them, and participate in the political system to make sure that we are all doing what we can to help achieve a good quality of life for ourselves and people all over the world.

Photo by Djordje Zlatanovic

Governments and other international agencies are also working on these issues. For example, the United Nations, along with other organizations, is working to achieve the Millennium Development Goals to address the issues of extreme poverty and hunger, education, equality, health, disease, and environmental sustainability.

THE USA IN THE SUSTAINABILITY PUZZLE

Many of the programs and technologies that help increase **sustainability** have come from the United States. However, because the average **ecological footprint** of U.S. citizens is the biggest in the world, many people also believe the U.S. footprint is unsustainable.[130] Evidence has also shown that, after a certain level, consuming more resources doesn't make people any happier.

The U.S. Footprint

The United States, with 292 million people, is the third most-populous country in the world and is growing by about 0.05 percent a year. This means it is adding 1.7 million people every year.[131] While that rate is relatively small, the United States is growing faster than any other major **developed country**. Many countries in Europe, for example, have growth rates of 0 percent. Experts predict that the United States could have more than 400 million people by 2050.[132]

This worries many people, because U.S. citizens have such a large ecological footprint—24 acres per person—that the global impact of U.S. citizens as a whole is very large. On average, U.S. citizens use many more resources than anybody else in the world.

Although U.S. citizens comprise less than 5 percent of the Earth's total population:

- U.S. citizens consume 26 percent of all oil and 25 percent of all coal.[133]
- U.S. citizens own about one-quarter of the world's automobiles—one car for every three people, including children.[134]
- U.S. cars alone create **carbon dioxide** emissions equal to the total CO_2 emissions of the entire Japanese economy.[135]

America's high rate of resource **consumption** has had both positive and negative impacts. On the positive side, the U.S. standard of living is high. Most people are able to meet their basic needs and enjoy many luxuries.

On the other hand, the United States' consumption level has had an impact on the environment. In the last 200 years, the United States has lost 50 percent of its wetlands, 90 percent of its northwestern old-growth forests, and 99 percent of its tall-grass prairies. In addition, 490 species of native plants and animals have become extinct and an additional 9,000 species are in danger of becoming extinct.[136]

Environmental damage does not happen equally in every part of the country. In fact, some of the activities that can do the most damage to the environment, and to the humans living in that environment, are concentrated in poor or minority communities. Data indicate that toxic chemicals are released and hazardous waste sites are located more frequently in low-income or minority communities.[137] This may be because citizens in those communities are discriminated against or are thought to have less political or economic power to fight such projects.

If you add together the footprint of all U.S. citizens, more than 6.7 billion acres are required to support them. However, the amount of land available in the United States to support these needs is only 3.6 billion acres.[138] This

U.S. citizens make up less than 5 percent of the world's population, but ...

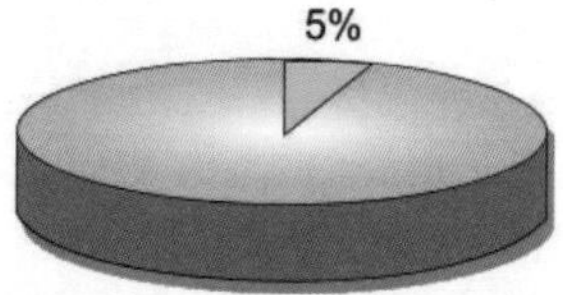

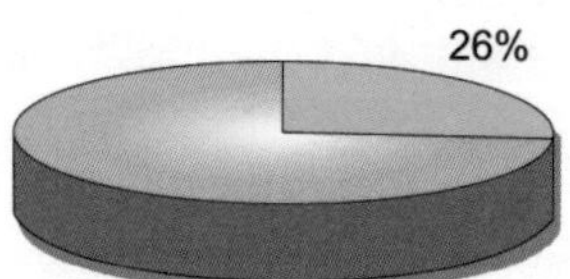

U.S. citizens use 26 percent of the world's oil.[144]

United States citizens' resource consumption percentages. Graphs by *Facing the Future: People and the Planet*

North American Grizzly Bear. Photo by Paul Bannick

means that the U.S. footprint affects other countries as well.

Some of the resources required to support U.S. citizens comes from within the United States, while other things are imported—food or timber, for example. Other impacts from America's footprint are exported. The United States sends some garbage to other countries, and the pollution created in the United States sometimes affects its neighbors, such as when factories in the Midwest cause acid rain to fall in Canada.[139]

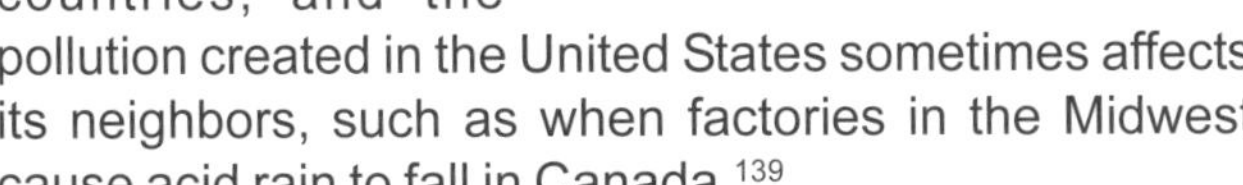

Encouraging Sustainability through U.S. Policies

Throughout its history, the United States has enacted policies that relate to each area of sustainability: economy, environment, and society. Some of these policies serve as examples to the rest of the world.

For example, to benefit society, the United States has passed national laws that restrict child labor in the United States. These laws limit the number of hours young people can work and bar them from working on extremely hazardous projects.[140] The United States also has mandatory education laws that require every citizen to complete a high school education and supplies teachers, schools, and materials in every community in the country.

The United States has environmental laws that help protect the environment and citizens' health. In 1955 the U.S. government passed the first national law to help fight air pollution. In 1970 the U.S. Environmental Protection Agency was founded to protect the air, water, and land within the United States.[141]

The U.S. government also works to insure that the economy is healthy and can provide jobs and opportunities for new businesses. It is often a difficult task to balance the needs of the economy, environment, and society.

Despite the United States' many measures that encourage sustainability, experts believe there are some U.S. policies that do not. Scientists sometimes criticize U.S. government policies because of our extravagant use of natural resources such as timber, oil, and freshwater.

For example, the U.S. Forest Service allows private companies to cut trees on Forest Service land. In 1997, however, the Forest Service reported that it lost $88.6 million on these tree sales. The agency actually spent money in order to allow private companies to cut trees.[142] Experts believe this practice encourages the unsustainable cutting of national forests and costs U.S. taxpayers money that supports private profits.[143]

The U.S. government also subsidizes the use and production of fossil fuels such as oil, gas, and coal. A **subsidy** is money provided by the government to keep the price of a good or service low. In fact, the government

U.S. citizens use 33 percent of the world's paper and plastic.[145]

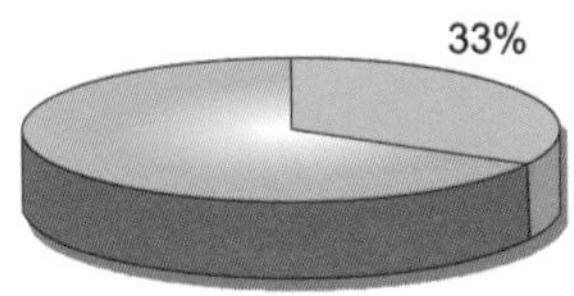

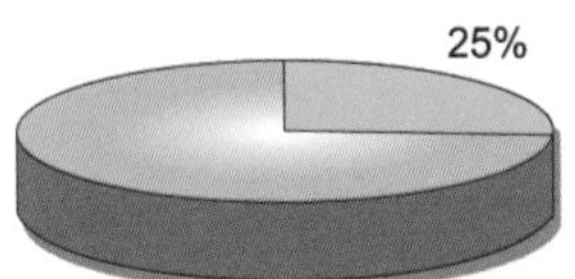

U.S. citizens own 25 percent of the world's cars.[146]

U.S. citizens produce 25 percent of the world's carbon dioxide emissions.[147]

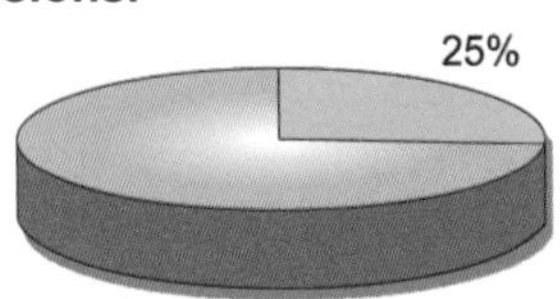

gives more than $5 billion each year to help these industries. Many of these subsidies allow companies to employ more people and conduct research on ways to limit the pollution caused by fossil fuels.

Photo by Chris Calwell

However, subsidies also create lower prices and encourage consumers and businesses to use more fossil fuels, which contribute to air pollution and **global warming**. The U.S. Environmental Protection Agency estimates that if those subsidies were eliminated, fossil fuel use would drop by 4 percent each year.[148]

Many of these policies are in place because they help private companies create jobs that help the economy. Others exist because of direct pressure from citizens or people's consumption choices. Overall, it is a difficult task to balance the need for a healthy economy with policies that also encourage sustainability. The good news is that a healthy economy, a sustainable environment, and a vibrant community can happen at the same time. It just takes a lot of thought and consideration in each step of the way.

Government policies that promote sustainable development, for example, by providing **economic incentives** for the purchase of hybrid or fuel cell cars, could improve sustainability by reducing air pollution while also supporting jobs in manufacturing these vehicles.

Citizens have a large role to play by letting their elected officials know that they support policies that encourage sustainability, by starting private projects that create economic growth and protect the environment, and by purchasing products that promote sustainability.

Are U.S. Citizens Happier?

Another critical issue that U.S. citizens can consider is whether the average high-consumption **lifestyle** makes people happier. Some people are concluding that it doesn't. In fact, one study showed that while income doubled between 1957 and 2002, the number of people who reported being "very happy" stayed at the same level.[149] Another study found that 75 percent of U.S. workers would like to have a simpler society with less emphasis on material wealth.[150]

The ability to consume is tied to having enough income to buy the things you want and need, which is also tied to the amount of time people spend working. No one in the world works more than U.S. citizens:

- The average U.S. citizen worked 199 hours more in 2000 than in 1973, an increase of almost five weeks annually.[151]
- The average U.S. citizen has ten days of paid vacation each year, while European workers get at least twenty-eight days.[152]

Our busy lifestyles are not only not making us happier, they can also do harm. Busy lifestyles, and the fast-food consumption that often accompanies them, can contribute to poor health conditions such as diabetes, high blood pressure, and heart disease. People also have less time to participate in their community, do volunteer work, or even vote.[153]

Researchers found common factors among people who reported being happy, including high self-esteem and strong relationships with family, friends, and community.[154]

How do you think the lifestyle choices you and your family make impact you and the planet?

We Are What We Measure

Often when we measure progress in the United States, a limited number of factors are considered. Many of these factors don't relate directly to peoples' well-being. People are often considered successful if they make a great deal of money. What if, instead, people considered success in terms of how happy people are, how much time they spend with their kids, or how often they volunteer in their community?

The progress of the United States as a nation is usually evaluated by the **gross domestic product** (GDP). GDP is a measurement of all the dollars that pass through the U.S. economy in a year. It is a measure of the growth of the economy.

However, this indicator doesn't necessarily indicate human progress or happiness.[155] Think about all the cars on the roads today. Every time someone buys a car or puts gas in it, the GDP goes up. Traffic accidents, hospital bills, and the lawsuits that accompany them also cause the GDP to go up, even though accidents aren't good for people. Cars and roads also cause air pollution and habitat loss because of the space required for the roads. Productive time can be wasted when people are stuck in traffic jams. All of these have negative impacts on people's well-being, but these are not included when calculating GDP. So while GDP measures dollars in the economy, it doesn't tell us everything about people's **quality of life**.

Many people say that we need better ways to measure how the United States is doing. One alternative to GDP is the **genuine progress indicator** (GPI). The GPI uses economic information such as the value of paid and volunteer work but subtracts things such as crime, pollution, and family breakdown. This helps evaluate whether people in the United States are truly better off from one year to the next by including quality-of-life factors, not just dollars spent. For example, between 1974 and 1994, the U.S. GDP rose by 79 percent, while the U.S. GPI rose by only 2 percent.[156]

Another measure is the **Fordham Social Indicator**, which calculates sixteen indicators of U.S. social well-being, including rates of teen suicide, people without health care, and income inequality. Between 1970 and 2000, while the GDP increased by 92 percent, the Fordham Social Indicator decreased by 29 percent.[157]

Groups around the country have come up with their own quality-of-life indicators to let them know whether their community is doing well and whether their environment is healthy. Some indicators include the level of youth involvement in community service, air quality, and the availability of affordable housing.[158]

What kind of indicators would you come up with to track progress in your community?

Immigration to the U.S.

Immigration—people moving to the United States—accounts for two-thirds of U.S. population growth.[159] People are coming to the U.S., both legally and illegally, from around the world. It isn't hard to see why. One survey found that illegal **immigrants** from Mexico could earn only $31 per week on average in Mexico compared to $278 per week in the United States.[160] That difference in salary is a big incentive for people to move over the border, even if they have to do it illegally.

There is a debate in the United States about how much immigration should be allowed. People who are against immigration claim that newcomers take jobs from U.S. citizens and use government services without paying taxes for them. People who say the United States should accept immigrants point out that, over time, new U.S. citizens contribute more to the country than they take. They also say that if we want to lower immigration, we need to address global poverty, discrimination, and conflict, which are the main reasons that people leave their own countries.

Immigration isn't new. In fact, throughout history, everyone but Native Americans came to North America from somewhere else. In the United States, immigration peaked in 1915 when 1.2 million immigrants arrived.[161] Where did your family come from?

The Way Forward

Many people are currently taking actions that increase the sustainability of the United States as a whole. For example, one group has proposed changes in our tax laws so that the government would tax pollution instead of income.[162] Other people have adopted business practices based on recycling all components of a product and have been able to increase profits and protect the environment.[163]

Cascade mountains in the Pacific Northwest. Photo by Derek Beauchemin

People are a critical piece of the sustainability puzzle. Citizens can let their elected officials know which policies they support, or they can run for office themselves. People can also examine their own lifestyles and ecological footprints. By asking, What increases my happiness and quality of life? people may be able to slowly make changes toward genuine progress.

SUSTAINABLE SOLUTIONS IT'S OUR FUTURE!

It's easy to feel overwhelmed, guilty, discouraged, or even angry when we hear about all the challenges in the world. However, there is good news. There are many actions that people can do to help build a bright and **sustainable** future. In fact, the most important solutions are things we already know about. We just have to decide—as individuals, communities, and nations—to do them.

Throughout this guide, we have seen how poverty limits people's choices and options. Not all people have the ability to take actions such as those listed below because they struggle just to meet their basic needs. However, as people gain more economic stability, they have more choices open to them.

Personal Solutions

Think About Your Future Family Size

Remember the concept of **ecological footprint**? A child born in the developed world is likely to use many more of the planet's resources than a child born in the developing world. What effects do you think an individual's choice about family size has on the planet?

Reduce Your Footprint

Every single day, everyone makes dozens of choices that affect their own ecological footprint. If you want to shrink your own ecological footprint, there are hundreds of ways to do it. The key is to know what actions have the biggest impact. When you're just getting started, it's a good idea to focus on the actions that make the biggest difference and not to worry if you can't do all the small things.

According to scientists who study human impact, the actions below are five of the most important ones you can take to shrink your footprint the most.[164]

Organic Vegetables. Photo courtesy of Oxbow Farm

1. Your Family Car —Transportation in cars and trucks is the single most environmentally harmful personal activity. To lessen your impact, there are two key things to do. First, research how many miles per gallon (its mileage) your family's car(s) gets. The higher the mileage, the better. Second, if your family is going to buy a new car, consider getting one that is fuel efficient and minimally polluting. Often there's a 50 percent difference between the most and least fuel-efficient cars.

2. Alternative Transportation—Whenever you can, use your feet, a bicycle, a skateboard, or a bus to get around. When you don't drive, you eliminate almost all of the pollution and greenhouse gases produced by your car or truck.

Bio-diesel bus. Photo by Stanford Berryman

3. Low-Impact Foods—The food we eat has almost as big an impact on the Earth as our transportation choices. **Consumption** of meat requires many resources. Overall, a vegetarian diet requires two to four times less land than a meat eater's diet.[165] That doesn't mean you have to give up cheeseburgers altogether! If you want to shrink your footprint, however, choosing to eat one less meal with meat each week can make a big impact.

4. Organic Food—Organic food helps the planet for many reasons. For one, it is grown without pesticides or fertilizers, which can contaminate water or soil and can make people sick. Also, organic farming can reduce soil loss and water use. Organic food can be more expensive than other food, which means some people can't afford it. However, as more people buy organic food the prices will likely go down, making it accessible to more people.

5. An Energy-Proof House—Do a survey with your parents of how much energy is used in your house, and then make energy-efficient changes when possible. You can begin by looking for places to install compact fluorescent light bulbs. You can also make a difference when you need to replace big appliances such as your refrigerator, water heater, washing machine, or clothes dryer. Look for the Energy Star certification to know if an appliance is energy efficient.

Ask How Much Is Enough

Another big question is deciding when you have enough of something. Is another gizmo really going to make you happier? Can you live just as well without it? Would the environment be better off without it? You don't have to deprive yourself of things you really enjoy. Just ask, How much is enough? and How do I want to spend my time and money?

Recycle as Much as You Can

Investigate your neighborhood's recycling services and start reducing the waste you send to the local landfill. Reducing waste and reusing materials helps the environment. Turning your food into compost is also a great way to reduce your trash, and if you have a garden, compost will help you grow your own vegetables.

Recycle! Photo by Gilda Wheeler

Flex Your Money Muscles

Vote with your dollars. You can put your money where your mouth is by supporting projects—and items—that are sustainable. In the United States alone, young people between the ages of twelve and nineteen spend $172 billion a year![166]

Think about what you buy and the companies you buy from. For example, does the manufacturer of your favorite clothing use sweatshop labor? Did the beef in your hamburger come from pastureland that was cleared from rain forest? If you want to change those practices, the best way is to tell the manufacturers and the stores selling those products that you can't support them and why. Let them know that if they want to keep you as a customer, they will have to provide products that don't hurt people or the environment. Economic pressure from consumers like you has caused huge companies such as Home Depot, McDonalds, and Starbucks to adopt more sustainable practices.

Many Pakistani villagers find ways to balance their own needs and the needs of the environment. Photo from International Snow Leopard Trust

Western Tanager. Photo by Paul Bannick

Get Political

The decisions we make today will determine the world we live in tomorrow. Getting involved as a citizen and looking at your country's national and international policies are key steps to achieving greater sustainability. It is up to engaged citizens around the world to lead the way in creating powerful changes toward sustainability. You can help educate your elected officials and media, point out the connections between issues, and remind them that you (and your family) will be voting on these issues now and in the future.

Think Big and Stay Informed

When you hear about problems in the world, ask yourself, What's the bigger picture? What are the underlying conditions? What are they connected to? You've seen in this guide how issues are connected and that many problems have several sides to them. Understanding these connections and different sides may help us find lasting solutions.

If you're looking for a place to get started on your own personal solutions, visit Facing the Future's website at www.creativeaction.org for ideas about how you can make a difference.

Global Solutions

You can make a difference on a global scale in lots of ways. Perhaps you want to get involved politically and write your elected officials. Maybe you are volunteering for a group that works with **refugees** from around the world. You could be educating your peers and others about these issues. Perhaps you have even decided that you will choose a profession that lets you work more on these issues.

Now that you have decided to get involved, what are policies and programs that can help support a sustainable world?

Primary Health Care

Providing primary health care around the world could lower infant and child mortality, increase life expectancies, and provide other essential services. In many parts of the world, infant mortality is so high that families often have more children in the hopes that at least a few will survive. If families had access to health care, which prevents most childhood deaths, many families would have only the number of children they wanted.

Reproductive health is an important part of primary health that allows parents to choose the number and spacing of their children. If reproductive health services were available to all families that wanted them, current population growth would drop by two-thirds immediately.[167] It's not very expensive to provide these services, and they allow people who already want to limit family size to do so safely.

Family planning "Come Let's Talk" session in India.
Photo by CCP, courtesy of Photoshare

Address Extreme Poverty

Poverty is related to population growth, environmental damage, migration, and many other issues. Ending **extreme poverty** would allow people to meet their basic needs and would have ripple effects on many other issues. Here are some global solutions to address extreme poverty:

- Provide debt relief to poor nations so they can spend money on development, not debt.
- Promote trade policies that don't unfairly favor producers in rich countries.
- Promote access to land, credit, and sustainable jobs so people can make a good living without hurting the environment.
- Support human rights so girls, women, and ethnic and religious minorities aren't left out of all these efforts.

Educate and Empower Women

Education benefits everyone, but educating and empowering girls and women creates particularly positive changes. The majority of the poor, hungry, and illiterate people in the world are female. In

ACTIONS YOU CAN DO TODAY!

- CONSIDER YOUR TRANSPORTATION CHOICES. Walk or ride your bike. Every time you get out of the car, you prevent carbon dioxide from being produced, lessening air pollution and global warming. If you or your family needs a new car, consider buying one that is fuel efficient.
- EAT LOWER-IMPACT FOODS. It takes much more resources to produce meat than it does to grow grains or vegetables, and less waste is produced too.
- SAVE ENERGY. Turn off lights, install compact fluorescent bulbs, and when your family needs to replace appliances, buy ones that are energy efficient.
- CREATE LESS WASTE. Reduce how much waste you produce. Buy products without excessive packaging. When you are through using something, recycle it, take it to a thrift store, or figure out a way to reuse it. Try composting your food scraps to really cut the amount of trash you send to the landfill.
- THINK ABOUT WHAT MAKES YOU HAPPY. Before buying something new, consider whether it will make you happier. What else can you do to be happy that doesn't require buying something new?
- VOTE WITH YOUR DOLLARS. Support sustainable businesses and products.
- GET POLITICAL. Write a letter to your elected politician or your local newspaper and let them know what you think. When you are old enough to do so, vote every time you have the chance. This is your right and responsibility as a citizen.

much of the world, girls and women do most of the work but receive less pay and less food. In some places, women can't own land, borrow money, or even plant trees to restore the environment without permission from men.

For every year a girl or woman goes to school, the more likely she is to have a smaller family. This improves the odds she'll have healthy kids and send those kids to school. She'll probably have a higher income and more power in her family and community.[168] Educating and empowering girls and women helps slow population growth, protect the environment, and reduce poverty.[169]

Change Our Minds

Most people are familiar with the solutions in this chapter. We know that recycling can save resources. We know that sending girls to school is good. We know that ending hunger and poverty and saving rain forests are all important.

But somehow, even though we know all these actions should happen, they are either not happening or not happening fast enough. Why is this? It's not because we're stupid. It's not because we're evil or because we just don't know any better. It's because we have deeply ingrained ideas about how the world works. Many people call this our **worldview**.

People's worldviews have developed over thousands of years as humans learned how to survive and thrive. Many people learned throughout history that when their society was successful, their population could grow and expand. People also learned that they could get resources from the environment to help them survive. These beliefs about population growth and resource use became part of many worldviews around the planet.

Increasing our population and using the environment helped us succeed in the past, but many trends indicate that we may soon hit natural limits to the number of people and consumption of resources on the planet. Some people even say that we are beyond the limits and living in an unsustainable way. What do you think?

If it is true that there are natural limits to how much we can grow or how much we can consume, how can we change our worldview to match this?

Working Toward a Sustainable Future

We can stabilize world population at a sustainable level. We can protect the environment. We can balance the most destructive inequities between nations, individuals, and genders. We have the knowledge, the technology, and the money to do all this.

Helping create a vision of a positive future for people and the planet is the first step toward creating that future. It provides a road map to guide us to that future. It tells us what we'll need to do to leave a just, secure, and sustainable world for our children and our grandchildren.

WHAT FUTURE WILL YOU CHOOSE?

Photo by Djordje Zlatanovic

GLOSSARY

aquifer—A naturally occurring underground geologic formation that stores a significant amount of freshwater.

basic sanitation—Safe and clean freshwater and a safe means of getting rid of human waste and garbage.

BCE (Before Common Era)—The term used in place of BC (Before Christ) to describe the period of time before the year 1.

biodiversity—The variety of life in all its forms, levels, and combinations, including ecosystem diversity, species diversity, and genetic diversity.

carbon dioxide (CO_2)—A greenhouse gas that is a by-product of burning fossil fuels.

carrying capacity—The maximum population that an environment can support.

CE (Common Era)—The term used in place of AD (Anno Domini, Latin for "in the year of the lord") to describe the period of time after the year 1.

consumption—The process of using natural resources, materials, or finished products to satisfy human wants or needs.

developed countries—The United Nations' term for those countries with a high average per-person income. Developed countries include Japan, Canada, the United States, Australia, New Zealand, and countries in western Europe. See also the sidebar "What's in a Name?" in Chapter 1 for a detailed discussion of this and other terms used to describe different countries.

developing countries—The United Nations' term for those countries with a low average per-person income. Developing countries include all countries except those in the former U.S.S.R. and eastern Europe and those countries that are considered developed. See also the sidebar "What's in a Name?" in Chapter 1 for a detailed discussion of this and other terms used to describe different countries.

ecological deficit—What occurs when we use resources more quickly than they can be renewed.

ecological footprint—The area of the Earth's productive surface that it takes to support everything a person uses.

economic incentives—Government actions, such as tax breaks, that promote certain policies, such as sustainable development.

environmental justice—The equitable treatment of all people, regardless of race, income, culture, or social class, with respect to the development, implementation, and enforcement of environmental laws, regulations, and policies.

environmental scarcity—When there just isn't enough of a resource to go around. See also structural scarcity.

exponential growth—A rate of growth in which a constant doubling occurs over time.

extreme poverty—The term for the conditions under which people live on the equivalent of $1 U.S. a day or less.

Fordham Social Indicator—A calculation of sixteen indicators of U.S. social well-being.

genuine progress indicator (GPI)—A measurement of quality of life that combines economic measures with indicators of social well-being.

global issues—Significant issues that are interconnected, occur across political and social boundaries, and affect large numbers of people and environments.

global warming—A change in global temperatures that scientists believe is caused by human activities.

globalization—(1) The closer integration of the countries of the world, especially the increased level of trade and movements of capital. (2) The expansion of global linkages and the organization of social life on a global scale.

green revolution—Agricultural practices and technologies started in the 1950s to increase food production through the use of machines, fertilizer, pesticides, irrigation, and the growth of hybrid varieties of rice, wheat, and corn.

greenhouse gases—Specific gases and chemicals, including carbon dioxide, that accumulate in the atmosphere and lead to global warming.

gross domestic product (GDP)—The total value of goods and services produced by and within a country.

gross national income (GNI)—The total income of a country's residents.

immigrants—People who move from one country to another for economic opportunities and social reasons.

infrastructure—The basic facilities and services for the functioning of a community or society, such as transportation and communications systems, water and power systems, and public institutions.

internally displaced people—People who are forced to leave their homes because of conflict, food scarcity, or other crisis but who remain within their country.

Kyoto Protocol—An international agreement, reached in 1997 in Kyoto, Japan, that extends the commitments of the United Nations Framework Convention on Climate Change. In particular, it sets targets for future carbon dioxide emissions by developed countries.

lifestyle—How people live, how they spend their money, and how they use their time.

nonrenewable resource—A resource, such as coal or oil, that cannot be replaced as it is used.

ozone holes—Gaps in the high atmosphere around the Earth caused by chemicals; ozone holes can allow harmful sun rays to reach the Earth's surface.

purchasing power parity (PPP)—When different currencies are compared to each other in terms of how much they buy.

quality of life—The level of well-being and the physical conditions in which people live.

refugees—People who have fled their country because they have a well-founded fear of persecution for reasons of race, religion, nationality, membership in a particular social group, or political opinion.

renewable resource—A resource, such as wind, trees, or fish, that can be replaced as it is used.

selective harvesting—A form of sustainable forestry in which only a portion of the forest is cut down each year.

subsidies—Money provided by the government to keep the price of a good or service low.

sustainability—Meeting our own needs without limiting the ability of future generations to meet their needs.
sustainable—Not using resources faster than the Earth can reproduce them.

structural scarcity—When there's enough of a resource to go around, but it isn't shared fairly. See also environmental scarcity.

Tragedy of the Commons—What occurs when a resource is owned in common, yet not managed in common.

worldview—A set of assumptions, perspectives, and beliefs held by individuals, cultures, and societies through which we make sense of our lives and our world.

ENDNOTES

Chapter 1: Sustainability

[1] Jared Diamond, "Easter Island's End," Discovery Magazine, 1995, http://www.hartford-hwp.com/archives/24/042.html.

[2] From the 1987 United Nations Brundtland Report's definition of sustainable development. G. Brundtland, Our Common Future, World Commission on Environment and Development (London: Oxford University Press, 1987).

[3] From the website for the International Institute for Sustainable Development, http://www.iisd.org/about/.

[4] United Nations Statistics Division's definition of developed and developing countries, http://millenniumindicators.un.org/unsd/mi/mi_dict_xrxx.asp?def_code=491.

[5] World Bank Country Classifications, http://www.worldbank.org/data/countryclass/countryclass.html, based on 2002 per capita gross national income.

[6] David G. Myers, "Happiness," in Psychology, 7th ed. (New York: Worth Publishers, 2004). See Chart 3 at http://www.davidmyers.org/happiness/Excerpt.html.

[7] At the United Nations Conference on Environment and Development (the Earth Summit) in Rio de Janeiro in 1992, 178 countries participated. Agenda 21 was adopted, with strategies to bring about sustainable development in the twenty-first century.

Chapter 2: What's *Up* With Population, Anyway?

[8] Population Reference Bureau, "2003 World Population Data Sheet." http://www.prb.org/Template.cfm?Section=PRB&template=/Content/ContentGroups/Datasheets/2003_World_Population_Data_Sheet.htm.

[9] Germany's population in 2003: 82,000 U.S. Census Bureau, http://www.census.gov; San Francisco's population in 2003: 764,000.U.S. Census Bureau http://quickfacts.census.gov/qfd/states/06/06075.html.

[10] Population Reference Bureau, "2003 World Population Data Sheet."

[11] The actual replacement-rate fertility is 2.1 children per couple, which takes into account deaths before children reach adulthood. In addition, even if the average number of children per couple dropped to 2.1 tomorrow, the population would continue to grow. This is because there are 1.8 billion people under age 15—nearly a third of the global population. Even if they averaged only 2.1 children per couple, they would add almost 2 billion people over time, and an equivalent number of people are not expected to die during that time. Thus, the total population would expand for some time even if the rate of growth was at replacement levels. For more information, see the section Momentum for Population Change in Population Reference Bureau, "Transitions in World Population," Population Bulletin, March 2004, p. 15, http://www.prb.org/Template.cfm?Section=PRB&template=/ContentManagement/ContentDisplay.cfm&ContentID=10110 and "Population Momentum," facts in Audubon webite, http://www.audubon.org/campaign/population_habitat/momentum.html.

[12] Population Reference Bureau, "Data Finder," http://www.prb.org/datafind/datafinder.htm. Based on birth rate of 22 per 1,000 and death rate of 9 per 1,000.

[13] Population Reference Bureau, "2003 World Population Data Sheet."

[14] United Nations Family Planning Association, "The State of World Population 2001," http://www.unfpa.org/swp/2001/english/ch01.html.

[15] World Wildlife Fund, "Living Planet Report, 2002." World Wildlife Fund, Switzerland, Average footprint for U.S. citizens is 23.95 acres, while average footprint for Indonesian, Peruvian, and Kenyan citizens are 2.79, 2.84, and 2.96 acres, respectively.

[16] Population Reference Bureau, "Iran's Family Planning Program: Responding to a Nation's Need," MENA Policy Brief, 2002, http://www.prb.org/pdf/IransFamPlanProg_Eng.pdf, and Janet Larsen, "Iran's Birth Rate Plummeting at Record Pace: Success Provides a Model for Other Developing Countries," Earth Policy Institute, December 28, 2001, http://www.earth-policy.org/Updates/Update4ss.htm.

[17] Population Reference Bureau, "2003 World Population Data Sheet."

[18] World Population Projections, Research Note 9 1999–2000, 19 October 1999, from Parliament of Australia website, http://www.aph.gov.au/library/pubs/rn/1999-2000/2000rn09.htm.

[19] "Use of family planning worldwide rose from less than 10 percent of married women in 1960 to about 60 percent in 2003" according to Population Reference Bureau, "Transitions in World Population," Population Bulletin, March 2004, p. 10, http://www.prb.org/Template.cfm?Section=PRB&template=/ContentManagement/ContentDisplay.cfm&ContentID=10110.

[20] Population Reference Bureau, "Transitions in World Population," Population Bulletin, March 2004, p. 6.

[21] United Nations Family Planning Association (UNFPA), "Characterizing Poverty," 2002, http://www.unfpa.org/swp/2002/english/ch2/page3.htm.

[22] UNFPA and Alan Guttmacher Institute, "Adding It Up: The Benefits of Investing in Sexual and Reproductive Health Care," 2004, http://www.ippf.org/resource/adding/pdf/Adding_it_up.pdf.

[23] Farzaneh Roudi-Fahimi and Valentine M. Moghadam, "Empowering Women, Developing Society: Female Education in the Middle East and North Africa," Population Reference Bureau, November 2003, http://www.prb.org/Template.cfm?Section=PRB&template=/Content/ContentGroups/Report/032/Empowering_Women,_Developing_Society__Female_Education_in_the_Middle_East_and_North_Africa.htm.

Chapter 3: Population Throughout History

[24] Population Reference Bureau, "Annual Increase in World Population," slide from PRB Graphic Bank, 2003, http://www.prb.org/Content/NavigationMenu/PRB/PRB_Library/Graphics_Bank/Population_Trends2/Population_Trends.htm.

[25] William Hardy McNeill, Plagues and Peoples (New York: Bantam Doubleday Dell, 1977), http://www.globalterrorism101.com/JustiniansPlague.html.

[26] Fact Index, "Black Plague," Wikipedia, 2004, http://www.fact-index.com/b/bl/black_death.html.

[27] Inventors Assistance League, "Chinese Inventions and Discoveries," 1999, http://www.inventions.org/culture/asian/chinese.html.

[28] Jared Diamond, Guns, Germs and Steel: The Fates of Human Societies (New York: W. W. Norton and Co., 1999), p. 411.

[29] Agency for Healthcare Research and Quality, "History of Smallpox," University of Alabama School of Medicine website, 2001, http://www.bioterrorism.uab.edu/EIPBA/Smallpox/history.html.

[30] GeoHive, "Regional population from 1750 to 2050," 2003, http://www.xist.org/global/linkg.php?xml=hist1&xsl=hist1. Data taken from United Nations, The Determinants and Consequences of Population Trends, vol. 1 (New York: United Nations, 1973), and United Nations, World Population Prospects: The 1998 Revision (New York: United Nations, forthcoming).

[31] Osamu Saito, "The Postwar Population Explosion and Asia," Asian Historical Statistics Project, 1996, http://www.ier.hit-u.ac.jp/COE/Japanese/Newsletter/No.3.english/saitoe.htm.

[32] The medium scenario in United Nations, World Population Prospects: The 1998 Revision (New York, United Nations, forthcoming).

[33] GeoHive, "Regional population from 1750 to 2050," 2003, http://www.xist.org/global/linkg.php?xml=hist1&xsl=hist1. Data taken from United Nations, The Determinants and Consequences of Population Trends, vol. 1 (New York: United Nations, 1973)., and United Nations, World Population Prospects: The 1998 Revision (New York: United Nations, forthcoming).

Chapter 4: How Many People Can the Earth Support?

[34] About 158 new people are born worldwide every minute. U.S. Census Bureau, http://www.census.gov/cgi-bin/ipc/pcwe.

[35] Based on 2000 data on footprint size; by hectares: India 0.77, Mexico 2.52, France 5.26, U.S. 9.7. From Redefining Progress, "Ecological Footprint of Nations 2004." http://www.redefiningprogress.org/publications/footprintnations2004.pdf

[36] Based on total available biocapacity of 11.97 billion hectares and total needed biocapacity for 6.3 billion people to each have a 9.7-hectare footprint of 61.11 billion hectares. From World Wildlife Fund (WWF), "Living Planet Report 2002." WWF International, Switzerland, 2002.

[37] WWF, "Living Planet Report 2002."

[38] Of the total average human ecological footprint of 2.28 hectares, 1.12 hectares are used for total energy use and of that, 0.99 is for carbon dioxide from fossil fuels. From WWF, "Living Planet Report 2002."

[39] These stories are based on interviews with Devin Hibbard in India and Kenya in 2000 and with Ian Byington in the United States in 2000.

Chapter 5: Global Trends—Food, Water, and Income

[40] United Nations Food and Agriculture Organization, "The State of Food Insecurity in the World 2003," ftp://ftp.fao.org/docrep/fao/006/j0083e/j0494e00.pdf.

[41] Lester R. Brown, Plan B Rescuing a Planet under Stress and a Cilivization in Trouble, Earth Policy Institute, 2003, http://www.Earth-policy.org/Books/PlanB_ch5_socialdivide.pdf.

[42] United Nations Food and Agriculture Organization, Towards 2015/30, (New York: UNFAO, Economic and Social Department, 2003), http://www.fao.org/english/newsroom/news/2003/14640-en.html.

[43] University of California at Davis, "What Is Sustainable Agriculture?" University of California at Davis Sustainable Agriculture Research and Education Program, 1997, http://www.sarep.ucdavis.edu/concept.htm#PlantPractices.

[44] Seattle Initiative for Global Development, "Building a Better World: A New Global Development Strategy to End Extreme Poverty," 2004, http://www.seattleinitiative.org/SIPolicyBrief.pdf.

[45] United Nations, "International Year for Fresh Water," UN initiative, 2003, http://www.un.org/works/sustainable/freshwater.html.

[46] Data from the New Internationalist magazine, no. 325, www.newint.org; United Nations Food and Agriculture Organization's website, http://www.fao.org; Environmental News Service, February 2002, http://www.enn.com; and Terry Leitzell, interview with author, 2004.

[47] Anne Platt McGinn, "From Rio to Johannesburg: Healthy Oceans Key to Fighting Poverty," World Watch Institute World Summit Policy Brief No. 5, May 21, 2002, http://www.worldwatch.org/press/news/2002/05/21/.

[48] Robert F. Service, "As the West Goes Dry,"Science, February 20 2004.

[49] Population Action International, "People in the Balance: Population and Natural Resources at the turn of the millennium," Update, 2003, http://www.populationaction.org/resources/publications/peopleinthebalance/pb_water.shtml.

[50] World Bank Vice President Ismael Serageldin, quoted in People and the Planet, "A Warning of Water Wars," People and the Planet 3, no. 5 (1996), http://www.oneworld.org/patp/vol5_3/intro.html.

[51] WorldWatch Institute, State of the World 2004 (New York: W. W. Norton & Co., 2004), p 47.

[52] WorldWatch Institute, State of the World 2004 (New York: W. W. Norton & Co., 2004), p 53.

[53] WorldWatch Institute, State of the World 2004 (New York: W. W. Norton & Co., 2004), p 55.

[54] United Nations Development Program, "Human Development Report 2002," p 17.

[55] WorldWatch Institute, Vital Signs 2003 (New York: W. W. Norton & Co., 2002), p 88.

[56] United Nations Development Program, "Human Development Report 2002," p 19.

[57] United Nations Development Program, United Nations Human Development Report 1998 (New York: Oxford University Press, 1998), cited by the Shared Capitalism Institute, http://www.sharedcapitalism.org/scfacts.html#Call54.

[58] WorldWatch Institute, Vital Signs 2003 (New York: W. W. Norton & Co., 2002), p 88.

[59] Seattle Initiative for Global Development, "Building a Better World: A New Global Development Strategy to End Extreme Poverty," 2004 pp. 5, 8, http://www.seattleinitiative.org/SIPolicyBrief.pdf.

[60] United Nations Department of Public Information, "The Feminization of Poverty," DPI/2035/A, May 2000, http://www.un.org/womenwatch/daw/followup/session/presskit/fs1.htm.

[61] A study of sixty-four countries with 75 percent of the global population found a significant correlation between GNP and subjective happiness until average annual income per person reached $13,000 (1995 dollars). After that, there was not a significant correlation between increased income and happiness. From Ronald Inglehart and Hans-Dieter Klingemann, "Genes, Culture, Democracy, and Happiness," in Culture and Subjective Well-Being, E. Diener and E. M. Suh, eds. (Cambridge, Mass.: The MIT Press, 2000), http://wvs.isr.umich.edu/papers/genecult.pdf.

[62] WorldWatch Institute, Vital Signs 2003 (New York: W. W. Norton & Co., 2002), p 88.

[63] Seattle Initiative for Global Development, "Building a Better World: A New Global Development Strategy to End Extreme Poverty," 2004, pp. 5, 8, http://www.seattleinitiative.org/SIPolicyBrief.pdf.

[64] Data on population and Gross National Income Purchasing Power Parity from Population Reference Bureau, "2003 World Population Data Sheet."

Chapter 6: Environmental Sustainability

[65] E. O. Wilson, The Diversity of Life (New York: W. W. Norton & Co., 1999).

[66] U.S. Environmental Protection Agency, "U.S. Climate Action Report 2002," p 4, http://yosemite.epa.gov/oar/globalwarming.nsf/UniqueKeyLookup/SHSU5BNPYJ/$File/ch1.pdf.

[67] E. O. Wilson, The Diversity of Life (New York: W. W. Norton & Co., 1999).

[68] World Watch Institute, State of the World 2004 (New York: W. W. Norton & Co., 2004), p 16.

[69] Joseph Spiedel, "Environment and Health: Population, Consumption and Human Health," Canadian Medical Association Journal, September 5, 2000, p 551, http://big.berkeley.edu/ifplp.envirohealth.pdf.

[70] We have lost almost 3 billion hectares of forest, according to the World Resource Institute website, 1997, http://forests.wri.org/pubs_description.cfm?PubID=2619.

[71] U.S. Department of Energy website, 1997, http://www.eia.doe.gov/oiaf/1605/vr96rpt/chap5.html.

[72] Musokotwane Environment Resource Centre for Southern Africa, "CEO Factsheet Series 12: Energy Sources and Uses," http://www.sardc.net/Imercsa/Programs/CEP/Pubs/CEPFS/CEPFS12.htm.

[73] World Watch Institute, "Accelerating Demand for Land Wood, and Paper Pushing World's Forests to the Brink," April 1998, http://www.worldwatch.org/press/news/1998/04/04/.

[74] Wulf Killmann, Gary Q. Bull, Olaf Schwab, and Reino E. Pulkki, "Reduced impact logging: does it cost or does it pay?" an academic review of 266 studies in Applying Reduced Impact Logging to Advance Sustainable Forest Management, United Nations Food and Agriculture Organization International Conference 2002, http://www.fao.org/DOCREP/005/AC805E/ac805e0f.htm#bm15.

[75] Cost based on the report's average cost of 390 rupees (exchange rate in 2000 was 43.64 rupees to the U.S. dollar). United Nations Educational, Scientific and Cultural Organization, "Best Practice on Renewable Energy: India—Programme on Improved Smokeless Chulas," published sometime after 2001, http://www.unesco.or.id/apgest/pdf/india/india-bp-re.pdf.

[76] E. O. Wilson, The Diversity of Life (W. W. Norton & Co., 1999).

[77] Thirty-four percent of scientists surveyed believe that 20 percent to 50 percent of species will be extinct in thirty years, and 69 percent of scientists surveyed believe we are in a period of mass extinction. Louis Harris and Associates, "Biodiversity in the Next Millennium," 1998 poll conducted on behalf of the U.S. Citizen Museum of Natural History, http://research.amnh.org/biodiversity/crisis/crisis.html.

[78] Brooklyn Botanical Garden, "Vanishing Plants," 2004, http://www.bbg.org/gar2/topics/botany/con_vanishing.html.

[79] First articulated by Garrett Hardin in 1968. For Hardin's original article, see http://www.garretthardinsociety.org/articles/art_tragedy_of_the_commons.html.

[80] U.S. Fish and Wildlife Service, "Bald Eagle Biologue," USFWS Region 3, 2004, http://midwest.fws.gov/eagle/success/biologue.html.

[81] World Watch Institute, Vital Signs 2003 (New York: W. W. Norton & Co., 2002), p 74.

[82] For example, cumulative California vehicle emissions for nitrogen oxides and hydrocarbons are about 1.2 million tons per year in 2000, which is 200,000 tons per year less than 1990 despite an increase in vehicle miles traveled of 40 billion miles per year. California Air Resources Board, 2003, http://www.arb.ca.gov/html/brochure/history.htm.

[83] International Development Research Center, "Taking Control of Air Pollution in Mexico City," August 12, 2003, http://web.idrc.ca/en/ev-31594-201-1-DO_TOPIC.html.

[84] World Health Organization, "Bronchial Asthma," 2000, http://www.who.int/mediacentre/factsheets/fs206/en/.

[85] World Watch Institute, Vital Signs 2002 (New York: W. W. Norton & Co., 2002), p 142.

[86] National Institute of Health, "Asthma Statistics," data fact sheet, 1999, http://www.nhlbi.nih.gov/health/prof/lung/asthma/asthstat.pdf.

[87] International Institute for Sustainable Development, "An Ozone-Friendly Future: Full Restoration Possible by 2050," 2003, http://www.iisd.org/briefcase/ten+ten_success1.asp.

[88] Disaster Relief, "It's Official: 1998 Ranks as the Warmest Year on Record," January 14, 1999, http://www.disasterrelief.org/Disasters/990113Temps/.

[89] U.S. Environmental Protection Agency, "U.S. Climate Action Report 2002," p. 4, http://yosemite.epa.gov/oar/globalwarming.nsf/UniqueKeyLookup/SHSU5BNPYJ/$File/ch1.pdf.

[90] World Watch Institute, State of the World 2004 (New York: W. W. Norton & Co., 2004), p 17, Table 1-7.

[91] Arni Isaksson of the Directorate of Freshwater Fisheries, Iceland, E-mail to author April 1, 2004.

[92] World Watch Institute, Vital Signs 2003 (New York: W. W. Norton & Co., 2002), p 88.

[93] U.S. Environmental Protection Agency, "Environmental Justice Fact Sheet," 2004 http://www.epa.gov/docs/ARD-R5/ej/fact.htm.

[94] Population Reference Bureau, "2003 World Population Data Sheet."

Chapter 7: People and the Planet: What Is the Good Life?

[95] John Sewell, "The Realpolitik of Poverty," Environmental Change and Security Project, 2003, p 35, http://www.wilsoncenter.org/topics/pubs/commentaries_povsec_27-39.pdf.

[96] United Nations Development Program, "Human Development Report 2002," p 17.

[97] United Nations Food and Agriculture Organization, "The State of Food Insecurity in the World," 2003, ftp://ftp.fao.org/docrep/fao/006/j0083e/j0494e00.pdf.

[98] Jeffrey Sachs, "The Strategic Significance of Global Inequity," Environmental Change and Security Project, 2003, http://www.wilsoncenter.org/topics/pubs/commentaries_povsec_27-39.pdf.

[99] United Nations Family Planning Association, "Characterizing Poverty," 2002, http://www.unfpa.org/swp/2002/english/ch2/page3.htm.

[100] CBS News, "180 Million Unemployed Worldwide," January 24, 2003, http://www.cbsnews.com/stories/2003/01/24/world/main537799.shtml.

[101] David Suzuki, "Human activities give rise to new diseases," Environmental News Network, June 3, 2003, http://www.enn.com/news/2003-06-03/s_4695.asp.

[102] National Intelligence Council, "The Global Infectious Disease Threat and Its Implications for the United States," report, 2000, http://www.cia.gov/cia/reports/nie/report/nie99-17d.html.

[103] David Suzuki, "Human activities give rise to new diseases," Environmental News Network, June 3, 2003, http://www.enn.com/news/2003-06-03/s_4695.asp.

[104] Sen. Patrick Leahey, "Low Vaccination Rates in Poorest Nations Needlessly Claim Millions of Lives, Says GAO," press release, October 19, 1999, http://leahy.senate.gov/press/199910/991019b.html.

[105] Terry McGee, "Urbanization Takes on New Dimensions in Asia's Population Giants," Population Reference Bureau, 2001,http://www.prb.org/Template.cfm?Section=PRB&template=/ContentManagement/ContentDisplay.cfm&ContentID=3931.

[106] "AIDS in Africa," data from website, 2004, http://www.data.org/whyafrica/issueaids.php.

[107] David Haney, "AIDS Cutting Life Expectancy," Associated Press, July 10, 2000, http://www.aegis.com/news/ap/2000/AP000715.html.

[108] United Nations Wire Service, "HIV/AIDS: Infection Rate Soars Among South African Girls," March 9, 2000, http://www.unfoundation.org, cited at http://www.findarticles.com/cf_dls/m2872/2_26/62140826/p1/article.jhtml.

[109] United Nations AIDS, "Children on the Brink 2002," joint report on orphan estimates and program strategies, http://www.unaids.org/EN/resources/epidemiology/epi_recent_publications/childrenonthebrink.asp.

[110] United Nations AIDS, "HIV/AIDS in Africa," World AIDS Day, December 2000, http://www.unaids.org/wac/2000/wad00/files/FS_Africa.htm.

[111] National Intelligence Council, "The Global Infectious Disease Threat and Its Implications for the United States," report, 2000, http://www.cia.gov/cia/reports/nie/report/nie99-17d.html.

[112] "World Population Projections," Research Note 9 1999-2000, October 19 1999, http://www.aph.gov.au/library/pubs/rn/1999-2000/2000rn09.htm.

[113] Environmental Health Project, "Health and the Environment in Urban Poor Areas: Avoiding a Crisis Through Prevention," 1996, http://216.239.53.104/search?q=cache:JMMyQfkgfpoJ:www.dec.org/pdf_docs/pnaby450.pdf+urban+poor+worldwide&hl=en&ie=UTF-8.

[114] Population Reference Bureau, "Transitions in World Population,"Population Bulletin March 2004, p 14, http://www.prb.org/Template.cfm?Section=PRB&template=/ContentManagement/ContentDisplay.cfm&ContentID=10110.

[115] International Labor Organization, "World migration tops 120 million, says ILO," press release on Workers without Frontiers—The Impact of Globalization on International Migration (Cornell, N.Y.: International Labor Organization, 2002), http://www-ilo-mirror.cornell.edu/public/english/bureau/inf/pr/2000/2.htm.

[116] International Labor Organization, "World migration tops 120 million, says ILO," press release on Workers without Frontiers—The Impact of Globalization on International Migration (Cornell, N.Y.: International Labor Organization, 2002), http://www-ilo-mirror.cornell.edu/public/english/bureau/inf/pr/2000/2.htm.

[117] Amnesty International, "10 facts you should know about refugees," http://refuge.amnesty.org/htm/10facts.htm.

[118] Global IDP (Internally Displaced Persons) Project, "Internal Displacement: A Global Overview of Trends and Developments in 2003," http://www.idpproject.org/global_overview.htm#1.

[119] United Nations Development Fund for Women (UNIFEM), WomenWatch website, 1997, http://www.un.org/womenwatch/asp/user/list.asp?ParentID=3001.

[120] United Nations Development Fund for Women (UNIFEM), WomenWatch website, 2000, http://unstats.un.org/unsd/demographic/ww2000/edu2000.htm.

[121] United Nations Development Fund for Women (UNIFEM), "The World's Women 2000: Trends and Statistics," WomenWatch website, http://unstats.un.org/unsd/demographic/ww2000/overview.htm.

[122] Janice G. Raymond (executive director of the Coalition Against Trafficking of Women), "The Ongoing Tragedy of International Slavery and Human Trafficking: An Overview," hearings before the Subcommittee on Human Rights and Wellness of the Committee on Government Reform, U.S. House of Representatives, October 29, 2003,

http://action.web.ca/home/catw/readingroom.shtml?sh_itm=68f9a02ebd640b77783e0b2cb0e7684c.

[123] John Sewell, "The Realpolitik of Poverty," Environmental Change and Security Project, 2003, http://www.wilsoncenter.org/topics/pubs/commentaries_povsec_27-39.pdf.

[124] Future Harvest, "Four Million Killed in Post-Cold War Conflicts: Prospects for Peace Increase, Even in Poorest Countries, with Investments in Agricultural Research and Technology," 1999, http://www.futureharvest.org/news/02161999.shtml.

[125] Population Action International, "Water Scarce Countries," in Sustaining Water, 1993, http://www.cnie.org/pop/pai/water-14.html.

[126] Seattle Initiative for Global Development, "Building a Better World: A New Global Development Strategy to End Extreme Poverty," 2004, http://www.seattleinitiative.org/SIPolicyBrief.pdf.

[127] John Sewell, "The Realpolitik of Poverty," Environmental Change and Security Project, 2003, http://www.wilsoncenter.org/topics/pubs/commentaries_povsec_27-39.pdf.

[128] John Sewell, "The Realpolitik of Poverty," Environmental Change and Security Project, 2003.

[129] Farzaneh Roudi-Fahimi and Valentine M. Moghadam, "Empowering Women, Developing Society: Female Education in the Middle East and North Africa," Population Bulletin, November 2003, http://www.prb.org/Template.cfm?Section=PRB&template=/Content/ContentGroups/Report/032/Empowering_Women,_Developing_Society__Female_Education_in_the_Middle_East_and_North_Africa.htm.

Chapter 8: The USA in the Sustainability Puzzle

[130] Redefining Progress, "Ecological Footprint of Nations," Sustainability Indicators Project, 2004, http://www.redefiningprogress.org/publications/footprintnations2004.pdf.

[131] Population Reference Bureau, "2003 World Population Data Sheet."

[132] Population Reference Bureau, "2003 World Population Data Sheet."

[133] World Watch Institute, Vital Signs 2003 (New York: W. W. Norton & Co., 2002), p 34.

[134] World Watch Institute, Vital Signs 2003 (New York: W. W. Norton & Co., 2002), p 56.

[135] World Watch Institute, Vital Signs 2003 (New York: W. W. Norton & Co., 2002), p 56.

[136] New Road Map Foundation, "All Consuming Passion: Waking Up From the U.S. Citizen Dream," 1995, http://www.ecofuture.org/pk/pkar9506.html#acp-foot, cites World Resources Institute, 1993 Information Please Environmental Almanac (Boston and New York: Houghton Mifflin, 1993), p 159.

[137] "Environmental Defense Scorecard," 2003,

http://www.scorecard.org/community/ej-hotspots.tcl?ej_attribute_code=pop_poc&fips_state_code=us&tri_p=t&land_p=t.

[138] Based on an average footprint of 23.95 acres per U.S. citizen with 280.4 million people, compared to biocapacity of an average of 13 acres per person. World Wildlife Fund, "Living Planet Report," 2002.

[139] "The Canada-Wide Acid Rain Strategy for Post-2000," 1998, http://www.ec.gc.ca/acidrain/strat/strat_e.htm.

[140] U.S. Department of Labor, "Youth and Labor," 2004, http://www.dol.gov/dol/topic/youthlabor/.

[141] U.S. Environmental Protection Agency, :Timeline," 2004, http://www.epa.gov/history/timeline/index.htm.

[142] General Accounting Office, letter to Representatives Cynthia McKinney and George Miller, September 21, 2001, http://www.taxpayer.net/forest/learnmore/govreports/10-23-01tspirs.pdf.

[143] Republicans for Environmental Protection America, "National Forests: A Heritage Worth Conserving," 1999 http://www.repamerica.org/policy/forests.html#Intro.

[144] World Watch Institute, Vital Signs 2003 (New York: W. W. Norton & Co., 2002), p 34.

[145] Mark Hertsgaard, Earth Odyssey: Around the World in Search of Our Environmental Future (New York: Broadway Books, 1999), p 196.

[146] World Watch Institute, Vital Signs 2003 (New York: W. W. Norton & Co., 2002), 56.

[147] U.S. Department of Energy, Energy Information Administration website, 2004, http://www.eia.doe.gov/oiaf/1605/ggccebro/chapter1.htm.

[148] Taxpayers for Common Sense, "Fossil Fuel Subsidies: A Taxpayer Perspective," http://www.taxpayer.net/TCS/fuelsubfact.htm.

[149] David G. Myers, "Happiness," in Psychology, 7th ed. (New York: Worth Publishers, 2004); also see Chart 3 at http://www.davidmyers.org/happiness/Excerpt.html.

[150] New Road Map Foundation, "All Consuming Passion: Waking Up From the U.S. Citizen Dream," 1995, http://www.ecofuture.org/pk/pkar9506.html#acp-foot.

[151] Five weeks of additional work is based on a forty-hour week. Juliet Schor, "The (Even More) Overworked U.S. Citizen," in Take Back Your Time, John DeGraaf, ed., San Francisco, CA, Berrett-Koehler Publishers, 2003, p 7.

[152] Joe Robinson, "The Incredible Shrinking Vacation," in Take Back Your Time, John DeGraaf, ed., San Francisco, CA, Berrett-Koehler Publishers, 2003, p 21.

[153] For more information on the loss of social capital, see Robert Putnam, Bowling Alone (New York: Simon & Schuster, 2000).

[154] David G. Myers, "Happiness," in Psychology, 7th ed. (New York: Worth Publishers, 2004); also see Chart 3 at http://www.davidmyers.org/happiness/Excerpt.html.

[155] Redefining Progress, "The Genuine Progress Indicator Update 2000," Issues Brief, December 2001, http://www.redefiningprogress.org/publications/2000_gpi_update.pdf.

[156] Redefining Progress, "The Genuine Progress Indicator Update 2000," Issues Brief, December 2001.

[157] Thomas Prugh and Erik Assadourian, "What Is Sustainability Anyway?" WorldWatch Magazine, September-October 2003, p 18.

[158] Taken from the forty regional indicators created by community members through Sustainable Seattle, http://www.sustainableseattle.org/Publications/listindicators.shtml.

[159] RAND Corporation, "Global Shifts in Population," Population Matters project, 2001, http://www.rand.org/publications/RB/RB5044/.

[160] International Labor Organization, "World migration tops 120 million, says ILO," press release on Workers without Frontiers—The Impact of Globalization on International Migration (Cornell, N.Y.: International Labor Organization, 2002), http://www-ilo-mirror.cornell.edu/public/english/bureau/inf/pr/2000/2.htm.

[161] International Labor Organization, "World migration tops 120 million, says ILO," press release on Workers without Frontiers—The Impact of Globalization on International Migration (Cornell, N.Y.: International Labor Organization, 2002).

[162] Center for a Sustainable Economy, "Sustainable Economics Program," 2000, http://www.redefiningprogress.org/programs/sustainableeconomy/ETR.htm.

[163] "The Natural Step," 2003, www.naturalstep.org. For one success story, see the story of the Interface Corporation in Paul Hawkin, Amory Lovins, and Hunter Lovins, Natural Capitalism (New York: Little, Brown & Co., 1999), p 139.

Chapter 9: Sustainable Solutions—It's Our Future!

[164] Michael Brower and Warren Leon, The Consumer Guide to Effective Environmental Choices: Practical Advice from the Union of Concerned Scientists (New York: Three Rivers Press, 1999), p 85.

[165] World Watch Institute, Vital Signs 2003 (New York: W. W. Norton & Co., 2003), p 30.

[166] National Institute on Media and the Family, "Children and Advertising Fact Sheet," 2002, http://www.mediafamily.org/facts/facts_childadv.shtm.

[167] Estimates show that providing reproductive health would prevent 52 million births per year. United Nations Family Planning Association and Alan Guttmacher Institute, "Adding It Up: The Benefits of Investing in Sexual and Reproductive Health Care," 2004, http://www.ippf.org/resource/adding/pdf/Adding_it_up.pdf.

[168] Farzaneh Roudi-Fahimi and Valentine M. Moghadam, "Empowering Women, Developing Society: Female Education in the Middle East and North Africa," November 2003, Population Reference Bureau, http://www.prb.org/Template.cfm?Section=PRB&template=/Content/ContentGroups/Report/032/Empowering_Women,_Developing_Society__Female_Education_in_the_Middle_East_and_North_Africa.htm.

[169] Farzaneh Roudi-Fahimi and Valentine M. Moghadam, "Empowering Women, Developing Society: Female Education in the Middle East and North Africa," November 2003, Population Reference Bureau.